The BBC presents the 115th season
of Henry Wood Promenade Concerts

The BBC Proms are broadcast live on BBC Radio 3 and you can enjoy
regular Proms broadcasts on BBC Television throughout the summer,
including many in High Definition and 5.1 surround sound on BBC HD.
You can also listen and watch again at your leisure for seven days after
broadcast with the BBC iPlayer at bbc.co.uk/iplayer.

THE PROMS 1895–2009

The Proms was founded to bring the best of classical music to a wide audience in an informal setting. From the very outset, part of the audience has always stood in the 'promenade'. Prom places originally cost just a shilling (5p); today, standing places at the Royal Albert Hall cost only £5.00, and over 500 tickets go on sale for every concert there from an hour beforehand. Programmes have always mixed the great classics with what Henry Wood, the first conductor of the Proms, called his 'novelties' – in other words, rare works and premieres.

1895 The 26-year-old Henry Wood is chosen to launch the Promenade Concerts at the newly opened Queen's Hall, Langham Place; Wood conducts the Proms throughout their first 50 years **1927** The BBC takes over the running of the Proms **1930** The new BBC Symphony Orchestra becomes the orchestra of the Proms **1939** Proms season abandoned after only three weeks following the declaration of war **1941** The Proms moves to the Royal Albert Hall after the Queen's Hall is gutted in an air raid **1942** The BBC Symphony Orchestra shares the season for the first time with another orchestra: the London Philharmonic **1947** First televised Last Night **1961** First complete opera heard at the Proms: Mozart's *Don Giovanni*, given by Glyndebourne Festival Opera **1966** First foreign orchestra at the Proms: the Moscow Radio Orchestra, under Gennady Rozhdestvensky **1970** First Late Night Prom: cult pop group The Soft Machine **1971** First 'world music' Prom: sitar-player Imrat Khan **1994** The Proms celebrates its 100th season with a retrospective of past premieres **1995** The Proms celebrates its centenary year with a season of new commissions **1996** First Proms Chamber Music series; first Prom in the Park **1998** First Blue Peter Family Prom signalling a new commitment to music for families **2002** The Proms goes digital on BBC Four; on-demand listening begins online **2003** Proms in the Park reaches out to all four nations of the UK with the unique festive atmosphere of the Last Night **2005** Proms Chamber Music moves to Cadogan Hall, and Henry Wood's *Fantasia on British Sea-Songs* celebrates its centenary **2008** Proms Plus introductions expand to precede every main evening Proms concert; Doctor Who Prom brings the Daleks to the Royal Albert Hall.

THE BBC: bringing the Proms to you – in concert, on radio, on television and online bbc.co.uk/proms

BBC (1895 promenade concert, Henry Wood); Peter Joslin (Queen's Hall); Tim Anderson (Proms in the Park); Chris Christodoulou (Proms Family Orchestra, Promenaders); Mark Allan (Doctor Who Prom)

BBC PROMS

Cover illustration: Andy Potts. **This page:** Bibliothèque des Arts Decoratifs, Paris/Archives Charmet/Bridgeman Art Library (opera audience); AFP/Getty Images (Stravinsky); Mark Thomas/BBC (Purcell); DreamPictures/Getty Images (Bollywood dancers); Chris Christodoulou (Proms Learning); Chris Christodoulou (presenter's box)

WELCOME TO THE
BBC PROMS 2009

Last year's BBC Proms season drew record-breaking audiences and it was heart-warming to see such loyalty and enthusiasm in the crowds. This year we have been able to build on that Proms festival spirit. We have more concerts than ever before – 76 in the Royal Albert Hall, and a greatly expanded 19 Proms Chamber Music recitals at Cadogan Hall – while our wide-ranging Proms Plus series moves to the Amaryllis Fleming Concert Hall at the Royal College of Music. Our special festival days devoted to single themes continue this year, giving us all the chance to immerse ourselves in a particular area of music-making.

We also welcome a new group of featured artists who will appear in more than one Prom, displaying their range and versatility – this year, in addition to Stephen Hough (who performs all four Tchaikovsky piano concertos), they include Joshua Bell, Susan Graham, Steven Isserlis, Katia and Marielle Labèque, Mark Padmore and Carolyn Sampson. We will also repeat last year's innovation of presenting a FREE family Prom (26 July) as part of our aim to reach the widest possible audience.

INSPIRING MUSIC-MAKING, INTERNATIONAL ARTISTS

Rather than impose any overarching non-musical themes, our aim is – as last year – simply to present two months of outstanding and inspiring music-making, featuring leading artists and orchestras from the UK and around the world. There are, however, some musical threads – and the idea of Multiple Pianos is one of them, which is celebrated with a special day on 9 August (*see pages 64–66*). We have included some of the wonderful concertos for two pianos, and have risen to the logistical challenge of presenting two pieces for four pianos, too. One of these, Stravinsky's *Les noces*, overlaps with one of our major focuses this year, the complete Stravinsky ballets. It was 100 years ago that the great impresario Sergey Diaghilev first encountered the music of Igor Stravinsky, and the work he heard on that occasion, *Fireworks*, raises the curtain on the Proms this year (with Oliver Knussen's *Flourish*, sparked by the same work, opening the Last Night). This launches our special celebration of Stravinsky's music (*see pages 19–25*) – the first time that all of his ballets have appeared in one Proms season.

Stravinsky always acknowledged his debt to Tchaikovsky, and we have another Proms first this year, in featuring all four of Tchaikovsky's pianos concertos performed by a single soloist. Much-loved British pianist Stephen Hough, who takes up the challenge, presents his own view of these diverse and (apart from No. 1) unjustly neglected concertos on pages 42–45.

With the programming of Respighi's Roman trilogy (of which *Roman Festivals*, astonishingly, receives its first Proms outing) and the complete Mendelssohn symphonies (part of a broader celebration alongside his fellow anniversarians Purcell, Handel and Haydn, *see pages 28–33*) we are this season reinventing a grand Proms tradition of presenting complete parts of a composer's output. Rather like our special festival days, this gives us the chance to compare and contrast performances and see a composer's work in a fuller context, particularly with the help of our Proms Plus events.

We have special weekends this year, too, with two 10th-birthday parties. As I write this introduction, the situation in the Middle East is particularly tense and fragile. Daniel Barenboim and Edward Said founded the West–Eastern Divan Orchestra in 1999 – not, in the words of Barenboim, 'as a political project, but rather as a forum where young people from Israel and all the Arab countries can express themselves freely and openly while at the same time hearing the narrative of the other'. Ten years on, the orchestra has also become a powerful musical force, and this year we have a weekend devoted to it with two main-evening performances, a Late Night Prom and a Proms Plus Boulez performance (*see Listings, pages 139–140*). Barenboim's performance of Beethoven's *Fidelio* with the orchestra (using Said's narration) promises to be one of the highlights of the season. This need for us to understand each other and the different cultures of the world seems more vital now than ever before, and in this spirit I hope you will enjoy our Indian Voices day on 16 August, which reaches its boisterous conclusion with the first ever Prom devoted to the music and dance of Bollywood.

Tchaikovsky concertos (*pages 42–45*)   Susan Graham (PCM 2 and Prom 19)   Multiple Pianos day (*pages 64–65*)   Stravinsky ballets (*pages 16–25*)

FAMILIES, YOUNG ARTISTS … Creation and evolution

We will also have a Creation theme in our opening weekend, with Haydn's joyous oratorio *The Creation* followed by Stan Tracey's magnificent jazz work *Genesis*. In addition, there will be opportunities for children and families to enjoy our Darwin-inspired Prom, which we will present twice, on 1 and 2 August.

BBC Radio 3's New Generation Artists scheme is also 10 years old this year and we will welcome distinguished alumni as soloists on the First and Last Nights. However, Alice Coote and Alison Balsom are not the only NGA artists appearing this year: over the August Bank Holiday weekend there will be more than 40 NGA artists appearing as soloists and in different duo, trio and chamber combinations in a three-day, 12-concert extravaganza at Cadogan Hall (*see pages 48–51*). All this, along with a strong complement of talented ensembles featuring young artists – the National Youth Orchestra of Great Britain, the West–Eastern Divan Orchestra, Gustav Mahler Jugendorchester, Chetham's School of Music and massed choirs for Handel's *Messiah* – shows a delight in our role of helping to nurture the audiences and the musicians of tomorrow.

NEW CHALLENGES AND NEW MUSIC

In mounting festivals such as this, I owe a huge thanks to my magnificent colleagues in the Proms team who, each year, manage to rise to new challenges and do so with dedication, creativity, professionalism and good humour. Thanks, too, to the players, singers and management teams of our own BBC performing groups, whose excellent work is too often taken for granted. Without their high standards of performance (in particular of new works) the Proms would be much the poorer.

As ever, new and less familiar music is a vital part of our programming, shown by a strong line-up of commissions and first UK performances (*see pages 54–61*). Some of these help our Late Night Proms to achieve a special atmosphere of their own – this season the series includes performances of music by Louis Andriessen, George Crumb, Philip Glass and Michael Nyman, as well as two other featured composers this year: Sir Harrison Birtwistle and Sir Peter Maxwell Davies, who both celebrate their 75th birthdays. In the year of their birth, 1934, British music lost three major composers – Delius, Elgar and Holst – and we are marking this turning point in British musical history with a '1934' weekend devoted to their music (*see pages 36–38*). That year also saw the beginning of MGM musical production, so what better excuse did we need to invite conductor and arranger John Wilson with his remarkable orchestra to present a celebration of the great MGM musicals on 1 August?

Mark Thomas/BBC (Haydn); D. Ricardo (Barenboim); Getty Images (Indian dancers)

> I WAS CUT OFF FROM THE WORLD AND FORCED TO BECOME ORIGINAL

Composers of the Year (*pages 28–33*)

Daniel Barenboim (Proms 48, 49 and 50)

Indian Voices (*pages 68–69*)

At these difficult and uncertain times it is important to remember music's unique power to excite, console and inspire us. The current global financial climate shows little sign of easing and we are fortunate indeed to be able to hold our Promming ticket prices at £5 per concert for yet another year (cheaper still if you buy a season ticket!); most of the other prices have also been held at last year's levels. This means that, thanks to the BBC's continuing commitment – both ideologically and financially – the Proms remains one of the best value-for-money experiences anywhere.

GLITTERING ARTISTS ... brought to you wherever you are

Where other than at the Proms can you hear not only our leading British orchestras and choirs, but also a glittering array of visiting orchestras from Amsterdam to Zurich (taking in Budapest, Dresden, Leipzig, Lyons and Vienna along the way)? This unique offering, linking quality and accessibility, is alive and well, and continues to drive our approach to the Proms.

Of course, you can hear all the Proms live on BBC Radio 3 and online (as well as on the BBC iPlayer for seven days after the concerts). You can also see and hear the concerts in primetime television slots on BBC Two and BBC Four. So the original vision of Henry Wood for the Proms – to bring high-quality classical music to the largest possible audience – is as strong as ever.

With well-established star artists including Martha Argerich, Riccardo Chailly, Nikolaus Harnoncourt, Mariss Jansons, Yo-Yo Ma, Zubin Mehta, and Proms debuts from rising new conducting talents Andris Nelsons, Yannick Nézet-Séguin and Kirill Karabits, I hope you enjoy all the concerts – from our gala opening evening to the fun and celebration of the Last Night.

I wish you a warm welcome to the BBC Proms 2009.

Roger Wright

Roger Wright
Controller, BBC Radio 3 and Director, BBC Proms

MGM/Album/akg-images (Singin' in the Rain); Anne-Marie Le Blé (Coote); Chris Christodoulou (Royal Albert Hall interior); Shutterstock (Signpost)

MGM film musicals (Prom 22)   Alice Coote (Prom 1 and PCM 13)   A unique experience at the Royal Albert Hall

EDWARD ELGAR
FREDERICK DELIUS
GUSTAV HOLST

PETER MAXWELL DAVIES
HARRISON BIRTWISTLE

1934: England at the Crossroads (pages 36–38)

The BBC Performing Arts Fund is a grant-making charity dedicated to helping talented, aspirational individuals to build a career in music and musical theatre.

Recognising the role of diverse, non-professional groups in the musical life of the UK, in 2009 the Fund is also supporting the musical development of choirs and amateur musical theatre groups.

For further information and for details of how to apply, please see our website: bbc.co.uk/performingartsfund or email performingartsfund@bbc.co.uk

BBC
Performing
Arts Fund

Registered charity no. 1101276

COMELY CONDUCT
– OR, WHEN DO I CLAP?

Ian Hislop adds his voice to the debate on audience etiquette and the social mores of concert-going

In one of Gerard Hoffnung's wonderful cartoons (*left*), an inexperienced concert-goer claps at the wrong moment, receiving a superior stare from the listener to one side, and a reproachful 'Shh!' from the person on the other. Hoffnung was a tuba player as well as a cartoonist, and knew British audiences well. He published this cartoon in 1957 but the controversy over applauding in the middle of a musical work continues, and returned again in the online question-and-answer forum with Proms Director Roger Wright during last year's season. Would you believe it, there had been clapping in between Strauss's *Four Last Songs*, and whoops and cheers in between movements of Dvořák's Eighth Symphony? One complainant found such applause 'thoroughly annoying', and agreed with another that a note should be printed in this year's programmes to try to 'reduce this disturbance'.

But I am afraid I can't help sympathising with Hoffnung's clapper. I know that you are not meant to interrupt the unity of a piece – and Henry Wood, founder-conductor of the Proms, himself disliked applause between the movements of symphonies – but, given that half the audience now takes any pause as a cue to cough furiously for two minutes, I am not sure that mistakenly timed appreciation is so unforgivable. And what of those listeners rustling the pages as they follow their scores, or beating time on the arm of the seat, or humming along quietly (but not quietly enough)? Surely these count as greater crimes against concentration?

What exactly is the etiquette at the end of the piece anyway? How soon should you start clapping? If it is the close of a slow-moving finale and you begin too soon, then it appears you have not been transported by the brilliance of the performance and are some sort of philistine desperate for it all to finish. If it is a thrilling climax and you leave it too long, it suggests that you don't know how many movements there are in the piece, or that you can't count, or that you were asleep. And what other gestures of appreciation are appropriate? Cheering, foot-stomping, jumping to your feet (if you are not already on them as a Prommer) – all of which regularly occur at the Proms, apparently without prompting disdain from others in the audience? I am always slightly embarrassed by the calls of 'Bravo' (this is England, after all), but have been to concerts with people who happily shout 'Brava' to show that they have noticed the sex of the soloist/conductor, or even 'Bravi' to show that their grammar stretches to embrace the entire orchestra.

I know that all this can be distracting, but I cannot really join the tut-tutters. The Proms doesn't issue any instructions on when it is acceptable to clap, perhaps so as not to curb enthusiasm (particularly of those who are new to concert-going and might somehow pick up the idea that the whole business might be a bit stuffy and joyless). I think this is probably shrewd, and it is interesting that in a recent online concert etiquette guide, shushing errant audience-members was judged to be ruder than clapping in the wrong place.

Message 7 – posted by **littlesoandso**, Jul 28, 2008

I was one of those people who did mistakenly applaud after the third of the Four Last Songs. I did certainly feel like an idiot not least because of the handful of people who glared at me before mouthing the words 'There are four, not three.'

The truth was I didn't know the Four Last Songs until the First Night. Normally I'm not a big fan of Strauss's vocal works but I quickly found myself completely swept away by the performance. Consequently I forgive myself for applauding in error. I do hope others can.

This is a reply to **this message**

⚠ **REPLY TO THIS MESSAGE ▶**

The opera bored: lithograph by Charles Léandre (1862–1930) depicting uninterested listeners

As a courtesy to those who may have fragrance allergies, please avoid wearing heavy perfume or cologne.

From the etiquette guidance currently issued by one American opera company

It is no good the complainants appealing to tradition on this issue because history has not always been on their side. The earnest etiquette of the concert hall is largely a 20th-century phenomenon. In the 18th century you arrived late, left early and talked throughout the performance. And the composers certainly had no objection to the audience showing their appreciation. Mozart recounted in letters how thrilled he was when audiences reacted in the middle of his works. Even in the 19th century Brahms admitted that he was disappointed by the silences after the first two movements of his First Piano Concerto and had hoped for a better response. Over the centuries the aristocratic chatter gave way to a more bourgeois respect for the music (and the musicians) and Alex Ross, music critic of *The New Yorker*, has expertly charted the development of this solemn, 'temple of music' approach, pointing the finger along the way at Wagner-lovers (with their 'Bayreuth Hush') and the conductor Leopold Stokowski, who in the 1920s tried to stop audiences applauding at all, not just mid-opus. ▶

EDINBURGH INTERNATIONAL FESTIVAL

REVEALED. OUR SUMMER COLLECTION

Handel's *Judas Maccabaeus,* **Verdi's** *Macbeth,* **Bach's** *Actus tragicus,* **Mendelssohn's** *Elias,* **Purcell's** *The Fairy Queen,* **Monteverdi's** *Il ritorno d'Ulisse in patria,* **Handel's** *Rinaldo,* **Elgar's** *The Dream of Gerontius,* **Berlioz's** *Roméo et Juliette,* **Handel's** *Acis and Galatea,* **Wagner's** *Der Fliegende Holländer,* **Handel's** *Admeto, Rè di Tessaglia.*

Sir Willard White, Philippe Herreweghe, **Arditti Quartet,** Orchestre des Champs-Élysées, **Lisa Milne,** Bach Collegium Japan, **Hamburg State Opera,** Nicholas McGegan, **Jordi Savall,** Bejun Mehta, **Sir John Eliot Gardiner,** Hopkinson Smith, **Orchestra of the Age of Enlightenment,** Lewis Psalm Singers, **Emerson String Quartet,** Andreas Staier, **Elisabeth Leonskaja,** European Union Baroque Orchestra, **Sir Charles Mackerras,** Quatuor Mosaïques, **Chiara Banchini,** Tonhalle Orchestra Zurich, **Esa-Pekka Salonen,** Dawn Upshaw, **Ivo Pogorelich,** Donald Runnicles, **Deutsches Symphonie-Orchester Berlin,** The Monteverdi Choir, **the Hallé,** Huelgas Ensemble, **Ricercar Consort,** Cantus Cölln, **The Sixteen,** Sir Mark Elder, **Staatsoper Stuttgart,** Collegium Vocale Gent, **Ingo Metzmacher,** Christopher Maltman, **Hespèrion XXI,** Christoph Prégardien, **Bernarda Fink,** Christian Zacharias, **Sir Roger Norrington,** Bryn Terfel, **William Christie.**

For your free brochure call +44 (0)131 473 2000 or visit eif.co.uk 14 August - 6 September 2009

"STOP! STOP! STOP! THERE'S SOMEBODY AT THE BACK THERE NOT CONCENTRATING."

Pont (Graham Laidler)/Punch Ltd. (above left); Gerard Hoffnung/The Hoffnung Partnership (right)

Ross concludes that if you want total silence then you can always stay at home and listen to a CD.

The relative informality at the Proms is surely a requirement for a series that is, after all, founded on the idea of 'promenade' concerts. And even in 1961 Malcolm Sargent, while Conductor-in-Chief of the Proms, said that the audience was 'young, keen, enthusiastic, as if they were going to a football match'. This may not be so much the case now – and no-one wants to hear chants of, say, 'There's only one Simon Rattle' or 'You're Shostakovich and you know you are' arise from the Arena. But Sargent did have a point about enthusiasm, and in the Royal Albert Hall you can witness the unique British take on concert-going high-seriousness – in the form of the Promenaders. They have their own traditions of vocal intervention and yet no-one could call them irreverent. Foreign conductors and orchestras are continually surprised that the same people who are happy to stand in rapt concentration through the most demanding music are the ones who also chant jokes in unison at them. They are the ones who shout 'Heave … Ho' when the stagehand lifts the piano lid, who

applaud when the orchestra leader sounds the A on the piano for the players to tune to, and who once collectively asked a choir stranded on the Royal Albert Hall stage for some minutes before their orchestra joined them to perform a Mahler symphony: 'Do you know the *a cappella* version?' To be honest, it is these very people – regularly praised by visiting conductors for their musical knowledge – who find it difficult to bob up and down in time to sea-shanties … but then it is better not to get on to the subject of the Last Night. That way madness lies. The point is that the ethos of the Proms, the sense of a great festival of music, is surely more important to cultivate rather than worrying too much about the qualities of reverence. Yes to seriousness and concentration, but no to sacralisation. 'It isn't church', as one critic said (and if you've been to church recently you'll have seen that most services nowadays are not nearly as formal as some concerts anyway).

For me, the most telling aspect of the discussions about inappropriate applause last year was that there were no complaints from the performers. Their concentration on the task of playing their instruments (rather than just listening to them) seemed to be unhampered. There is another Hoffnung cartoon called 'Enthusiast' (*right*) depicting a young man standing on his seat and wildly applauding. One neighbour looks mildly bored but the other smiles benignly at him. That's the spirit. ●

Members are required to applaud
immediately after sublime codas
and cough distinctly
during expressive silences
Distinct coughing is of
paramount importance
to stifle or muffle it
forbidden on pain of expulsion

From a poem by Alfred Brendel, musing on an alliance of Cologne's Coughers and Clappers (published in *One Finger Too Many*, Faber and Faber)

BBC *Concert* ORCHESTRA

The heart of great music

Be the first to hear about our events and broadcasts

Join the BBC Concert Orchestra free mailing list. Email, text or call us with your contact details:

Email **concert.orch@bbc.co.uk**
Text **BBC CO to 83111**
Call **020 8752 4676**

bbc.co.uk/concertorchestra

STRAVINSKY
MASTER OF THE DANCE

In the centenary year of Stravinsky's first collaboration with Diaghilev's Ballets Russes, Stephen Walsh surveys the iconoclast's 11 ballet scores originally written for the stage – all of them appearing at the Proms – whose influences range from pagan Russian ritual to Greek myth … to a game of poker

Eleven ballet scores by one composer in a single season: that's remarkable, not just for the fact that Stravinsky wrote so many pure dance works, but particularly for the fact that, almost 40 years after his death, they all still seem so worth hearing without the dance that brought them into being. From the start Stravinsky's music seems to flow through the body in a way that other composers' does not – though that's a moot point: who can say that Bach, Mozart, Beethoven, Mendelssohn did not write body music? In the end, all music is movement. What Stravinsky did was to treat that property once again as starting point, rather than mere axiom.

He came to ballet in the first place quite by chance. He once described (to former Proms Director, the late John Drummond) how one day he was summoned by Sergey Diaghilev in St Petersburg in 1909 after a performance of his orchestral piece *Fireworks*, waited for 20 minutes in the

Stravinsky: 'I love and am interested in ballet most of all, and this is no empty enthusiasm, but a serious and profound delight in theatrical spectacle – as living visual art.'

entrance hall to Diaghilev's apartment and was about to make for the exit when the great impresario suddenly appeared and ushered him inside. 'You know, my dear,' he told Drummond, 'I've often wondered, if I'd opened that door, whether I would have written *The Rite of Spring*.'

Would he even have written *The Firebird*? In St Petersburg Stravinsky had been brought up in a musical tradition that was aggressively operatic. His teacher, Rimsky-Korsakov, had composed some 15 operas and hardly a whiff of ballet music. Ballet, indeed, was routinely despised in Rimsky circles, notwithstanding the brilliance of Tchaikovsky's two late ballets, *The Sleeping Beauty* and *The Nutcracker*, of recent memory. It was a genre associated with Mariinsky Theatre matinees, with curiously hybrid audiences of children with their governesses, and men in raincoats; musically it was beneath contempt, usually based on what the critic Walter Nouvel called 'Russian salads' – sequences of pieces lifted from different works and, if necessary, reorchestrated. Even Diaghilev depended to some extent on this kind of thing; what else after all (though not Russian) was the Chopin ballet *Les sylphides*? In 1910 he made a ballet out of Rimsky's *Sheherazade*, leaving out the slow movement and provoking a rage of threatened litigation on the part of the late composer's family.

The following year Stravinsky wrote to Rimsky-Korsakov's son Vladimir one of his finest letters, defending ballet against the prim reproaches of the Rimsky school. 'I'm simply perplexed that you, who so loved the plastic arts and were so keenly interested in painting and sculpture, can pay so little attention to choreography – the third type of plastic art, and the one form of theatre which sets itself the basic goal of beauty and nothing more, just as Michelangelo's sole aim was the beauty of the visible.' Whether or not Vladimir, still seething at the abuse of *Sheherazade*, would have regarded Stravinsky's own current project, *The Rite of Spring*, as aiming at 'beauty and nothing more' is a vain question. By that time Stravinsky was free of St Petersburg and its narrow prescriptions.

His remarks about ballet, all the same, need more context. The Ballets Russes, which first appeared (not yet under ▶

Firebird costume design for the premiere in 1910

The Firebird (1910) Prom 16

First performance Théâtre Nationale de l'Opéra, Paris
Company Ballets Russes
Choreographer Mikhail Fokine
Scenery/Costumes Alexander Golovine/Golovine & Léon Bakst

The plot, devised by the choreographer Fokine with help from Diaghilev's other collaborators, is standard 19th-century Russiana, stereotyped for the Paris market. A prince strays into the forest domain of the demon Kashchey. He captures the Firebird (*above*) and, in return for her release, is helped by her to break the egg which contains Kashchey's soul, destroy his power and free the princesses he holds captive; the most beautiful of these the prince marries. The music likewise draws heavily on Russian sources – folksong, Glinka, Borodin, Glazunov, Stravinsky's teacher Rimsky-Korsakov, and even his contemporary Scriabin – but somehow personalises this material, while handling it with such brilliance that one forgets the derivations. It remained Stravinsky's most popular score, a fact he resented since it earnt him no royalties.

The Open University

I had a love affair with a statue

OK, it wasn't just a statue, it was anything to do with ancient Greece. But it was a love affair all the same.

"I guess you could say I've always been fascinated by ancient history – it just took me a long time to do something about it! As a girl, I remember spending hours in the British Museum just staring at Greek pots. I used to wonder about the people who'd made them and what life was like then.

Kija Bowerman
Humanities student

The thing is, it was only many years later when my husband – who'd seen The Open University on TV – said, "Why don't we both do a degree course?" I thought "why not?" and this led to a foundation course in social sciences, which developed into a degree in humanities including Ancient Greek.

It's been a true voyage of discovery for me – literally – I haven't just studied the course, I've travelled and discovered the real Greece, and even learned to speak both modern and Ancient Greek. I'm living proof that it's never too late to fulfill your ambitions – all thanks to the support and sense of community the OU has given me. Quite frankly my life would be dull and boring without it!"

Amazing thing, inspiration

Why choose the The Open University?

Our innovative method of supported open learning enables you to study wherever and whenever you like with one to one help from your tutor.

We offer over 570 courses, developed by leading experts. Subject areas in Arts and Humanities include:

- Classical Studies • English
- History • History of Art • Music
- Philosophy • Religious Studies

Inspired? Get a prospectus...

0845 300 8845

Quote: AAKAAA when you call us or go online
www.openuniversity.co.uk/support

INSPIRING LEARNING

Stravinsky with Diaghilev (*right*) in 1926, after his first journey by plane, from Paris to Croydon

T. P./Lebrecht Music & Arts (above left); Bill Cooper/Birmingham Royal Ballet (below left); Steve Hanson/Birmingham Royal Ballet (above right)

Petrushka (1911) Prom 15

First performance Théâtre du Châtelet, Paris
Company Ballets Russes
Choreographer Mikhail Fokine
Scenery/Costumes Alexander Benois

Petrushka evolved from a pair of piano-and-orchestra pieces inspired by a puppet show at the annual Shrovetide fairs in St Petersburg. The ballet idea was Diaghilev's; he wanted to distract Stravinsky from *The Rite of Spring* and persuade him to work with Alexander Benois. Half of the music is descriptive of the fair itself, with brilliant dances for local types such as wet-nurses, coachmen, the peasant with his bear. The other half is the tragic tale of the puppet Petrushka (*below right*), in love with the Ballerina (*centre*), who alas prefers the splendid Blackamoor (*left*). In the final scene the Blackamoor chases Petrushka out of the booth and kills him in front of the fairground crowd. Stravinsky's folksong-based music is seminal for his later harmonic, rhythmic and orchestral idiom, but its modernism goes by almost unnoticed in the speed and colour of the action.

Birmingham Royal Ballet, 2008

that name) in Paris in 1909, was by no means Diaghilev's first project, and in fact it was not even his idea. He had started out in the St Petersburg art world in the late 1890s by co-founding *Mir iskusstva* ('The World of Art'), a magazine devoted to art and design in the spirit of art nouveau and Arts and Crafts, and utterly uninterested in the realism and social questions that had been the preoccupation of Russian artists, writers and even musicians since mid-century. *Mir iskusstva* was pure art-for-art's-sake, studiously apolitical, conservative and, in a sense, old-fashioned, though the art it promoted was modern, even hypermodern. Diaghilev's *World of Art* colleague, the painter Alexander Benois, was obsessed, rather, with the 18th century as a vision of elegance and purity, and, as part of that obsession, with classical dance and the magical, non-realist subject matter to which dance seemed to lend itself. It was Benois who persuaded Diaghilev to turn his attention to ballet and to follow up his Paris concerts of 1907 and his *Boris Godunov* of 1908 (starring the celebrated bass Chaliapin) with an entire ballet season in 1909. The 1909 season began with *Le pavillon d'Armide*, planned and designed by Benois, choreographed by Mikhail Fokine, and with a sumptuous but derivative score by Nikolay Tcherepnin. But the rest of the ballet repertoire was Russian salad, and though Paris was thrilled by the dancers (Nijinsky, Pavlova, Karsavina, *et al*) and by the spectacular designs of Benois and Léon Bakst, it sneered at the music, including poor Tcherepnin's. 'The young Russian composers,' one reviewer wrote, 'need to get down to serious work in order to supply scores of a more personal character fit to be shown to us.' The reviewer, Michel-Dimitri Calvocoressi, can have had no notion what he was starting.

Diaghilev at once began the search for a composer whose music might measure up to the company's dance and design. He quickly commissioned *Daphnis et Chloé* from Ravel (though not for 1910). But the Russian field was unexciting: Tcherepnin himself, Rimsky's older pupils Glazunov and the notoriously lazy Lyadov. He even considered one of the younger Rimsky pupils, Fyodor Akimenko (who, as it happened, had taught Stravinsky ▶

Birmingham Royal Ballet, 2005 (recreation of original costumes and choreography)

The Rite of Spring (1913) Prom 38

First performance Théâtre du Champs-Élysées, Paris
Company Ballets Russes
Choreographer Vaslav Nijinsky
Scenery/Costumes Nikolay Roerich

For years *The Rite of Spring* was more famous for its first-performance riot than for its music, which was little heard before the 1920s. The primitive subject matter continued to be thought of as hypermodern. Yet the idiom was characteristic of late-Tsarist Russia, and is found in the paintings of Stravinsky's scenarist, Nikolay Roerich, and in the Symbolist poetry of the day. In a series of ritual actions, a young girl is chosen to dance herself to death to fertilise the soil for new spring growth. The music, too, was less off-the-wall than Stravinsky later made out. Its diabolical energy recalls works by Musorgsky, Borodin and Rimsky-Korsakov, while the compositional technique comes in essence from *Petrushka*. But what can explain the unique musical firepower? Only that hackneyed word, *genius*.

Pulcinella (1920) Prom 20

First performance Théâtre Nationale de l'Opéra, Paris
Company Ballets Russes
Choreographer Leonid Massine
Scenery/Costumes Pablo Picasso

The idea for these arrangements of instrumental and operatic pieces by Pergolesi and others (mainly 18th-century Neapolitan) came from Diaghilev and his latest ballet-master, Massine, and was partly designed to patch up a long-standing row with Stravinsky over royalty payments. Diaghilev probably expected simple orchestrations, and was mildly put out by Stravinsky's occasionally wayward harmonies and thrown rhythms. The audience at the Paris premiere in 1920 did not mind, however, and the production, with designs by Picasso and choreography by Massine, was |one of the Ballets Russes' most brilliant postwar successes. The plot itself – a piece of *commedia dell'arte* nonsense involving Pulcinella in a series of disguises to outwit his jealous rivals in love – is merely a peg on which to hang this delightful essay in musical and choreographic masquerade.

Costume designs by Vladimir Dmitriev, 1926

Les noces Royal Ballet, 2004

Les noces (1923) Prom 33

First performance Théâtre de la Gaîté-Lyrique, Paris
Company Ballets Russes
Choreographer Bronislava Nijinska
Scenery/Costumes Natalia Goncharova

Stravinsky thought of his wedding ballet in 1912, but it took him another 11 years to finalise, by which time he was writing neo-Classical works like the Octet and the Piano Concerto, a style which the eventual scoring for four pianos and percussion reflects. But truly *Les noces* is the purest product of his Russian style, exploring to an extreme of subtlety the rhythmic-colouristic world opened up by *The Rite of Spring* and by the authentic folk texts. The four tableaux depict the pagan elements of the peasant wedding, touching only peripherally on the church ceremony. But at the end bells chime to signal the moment of procreation with the four parents stolidly on guard outside the bedroom door: surely one of the profoundest, most moving episodes in modern theatre.

harmony). Then finally he remembered the young composer of *Fireworks*, who had done him some Chopin arrangements for *Sylphides* in the 1909 season, and he decided to take a risk. By this time it was already late autumn, and the untried composer had to write a one-hour ballet for large orchestra in six months. Fortunately, the plot and scenario had already been more or less devised, and Stravinsky could work in detail with the choreographer, Fokine, learning about ballet as he went along – about the difference between set-piece dance and pantomime or action music, about what dancers could and could not be expected to do. Nevertheless the achievement of so complex a score, on time and to such a degree of technical excellence, was an amazing feat, and one which Diaghilev was surely not entitled to expect. The spectacular success of *The Firebird* in June 1910 was no more than it deserved, and the press was everything Diaghilev could have wished for. Yet compared with what was to follow, it was much as Debussy said: 'What do you want? You had to start with something.'

For all its brilliance, *The Firebird* is quite a conventional score, much indebted to Russian sources, most of them unknown to Paris in 1910. But Stravinsky now performed a stylistic pole-vault without parallel in recent music history. Even before finishing *The Firebird* he was contemplating a ballet about human sacrifice (he tells us he dreamt the subject, but this may have been a story cooked up later to avoid having to acknowledge the scenario's co-inventor, Nikolay Roerich). Then that summer Diaghilev, who disliked projects that didn't depend on him, managed to sidetrack Stravinsky into turning some piano pieces he was writing into a ballet about a puppet in a fairground booth. Stravinsky may have needed little persuading. The sacrifice ballet was forbidding and might not get staged. The puppet ballet, *Petrushka*, was exciting and colourful and gave him the opportunity to experiment with new treatments of folk tunes in a harmonically and rhythmically straightforward context. *Petrushka* is indeed full of borrowed tunes and street cries (likewise unknown in Paris, though the work's first Russian audiences knew them all and heard the ballet as a set of arrangements). But what really makes it live is the astounding vitality of the rhythmic language, in which tunes are combined in patterns based on variable numbers of beat-counts and the barlines allocated accordingly, a technique co-opted by Messiaen, who called it 'additive'. Stravinsky later said that the success of *Petrushka* (in June 1911) helped him compose *The Rite of Spring* with confidence. And one can well believe him, because *The Rite* uses – admittedly in a more complex way – techniques tried and tested in the earlier ballet. Here, too, folk tunes (or phrases derived from them) are combined in ways that create dense and, in this case, harsh harmonies, and using additive rhythmic patterns that produce the work's notorious unequal bar-lengths. At this point, *The Firebird* might – symbolically does – belong to a different century.

It has never been necessary to insist that *The Rite of Spring* was a key work in modern music. Leaving aside

the (at first inaudible) fact that it is a masterpiece, the riot at its first performance made it famous. But Stravinsky himself drew conclusions from it that probably nobody else could have drawn. And it was these conclusions, rather than the violence or the din, that made it important as well as notorious. The first thing he did after the noisy Paris performances in 1913 (and after finishing his earlier opera *The Nightingale*) was to strip down the huge orchestra and begin working with simpler ideas and a more austere sound palette. He had already, before finishing *The Rite*, had his next ballet idea, this time based on another, arguably less disagreeable form of female sacrifice, the village wedding: *Les noces*. The trouble was that by the time he started composing it in earnest, war had begun, ballet performances were restricted, Diaghilev's Russian funds had dried up, and there was little immediate prospect of putting on a complicated new ballet. So instead Stravinsky tinkered with smaller things, songs, piano pieces, and a couple of hybrid theatre works – *Renard* and *The Soldier's Tale* – and meanwhile *Les noces* was completed (1917), then rescored (1919), then finally re-rescored (1922), down from a large chamber orchestra to its definitive version for four pianos and percussion (always with voices). Not until 1923 did Paris (or anywhere else) hear this wonderful ▷

Royal Ballet, 2007

Apollo (1928) Prom 39

First performance Library of Congress, Washington DC
Choreographer Adolf Bolm
Scenery/Costumes Nicholas Remisov

Originally written to a commission from the Elizabeth Sprague Coolidge Foundation and premiered in Washington DC in April 1928 with choreography by the former Diaghilev dancer Adolf Bolm, *Apollon musagète* (its original title) was probably always thought of by Stravinsky as a Diaghilev project. The Ballets Russes production opened in Paris two months later with choreography by Balanchine and Serge Lifar in the title-role. The choice of subject – the birth of Apollo, his ceremonial dances with the Muses, and his transfiguration onto Parnassus – suggests a stage version of Stravinsky's musical preoccupations of the past six or seven years: Classical balance and clarity, formal modelling, expressive restraint. But nobody could have predicted the placid, courtly tone of the music for string orchestra, so different from the immediately preceding, highly dramatic opera-oratorio *Oedipus rex*.

Stravinsky transcribes a peasant song while his mother holds his son, Theodore (1909)

Theatre Museum/arg-images (p20, left); Dee Conway/Royal Ballet (p20 main image); Theodore Stravinsky Foundation/Lebrecht Music & Arts (below right); Stephanie Methuen/Lebrecht Music & Arts (above right)

Le Baiser de la fée.
Alternative Winds.

Costume design for the Winds by Kenneth Rowell, Royal Ballet, 1960

The Fairy's Kiss (1928)
Prom 34

First performance Théâtre Nationale de l'Opéra, Paris
Company Ballets d'Ida Rubinstein
Choreographer Bronislava Nijinska
Scenery/Costumes Alexander Benois

So soon after *Apollo*, Stravinsky again reinvented himself. When Alexander Benois suggested arranging pieces by Tchaikovsky for an Ida Rubinstein commission in November 1928, he doubtless expected another *Pulcinella*. Perhaps Stravinsky did too, but he was overtaken by a creative impulse and found himself reworking and reinventing to the point where he nearly ran out of time. *The Fairy's Kiss* stands as a spectacular tribute to one great composer's critical admiration of another, a work of great musical wit and vitality, and an icon of the 20th-century urge to reinhabit history. The story, from Hans Christian Andersen, is like a 19th-century Alpine scene on the kitchen wall. A young child abandoned in a storm is found and kissed by the Ice Fairy, who years later comes back to reclaim him on his wedding day. But the music is quite another matter.

Jean Cocteau's sketch of Picasso supporting a stooped Stravinsky, the latter having consumed too much vodka following a performance of *The Rite of Spring*

music, by which time other, completely different works had intervened to confuse the already complicated picture of Stravinsky's artistic evolution.

This is the starting moment of so-called neo-Classicism. Instead of folk subjects and idioms, Stravinsky is now modelling himself on other, mostly earlier styles (though they include ragtime). The 'Classicism' itself is more a matter of generic description – cool, clear, balanced, formal – than of style as such. In fact his first substantial work of this type, the operetta *Mavra* staged by Diaghilev in 1922, is based on 19th-century Russian models. Before this, in 1920, Paris had seen *Pulcinella*, one of the most brilliant

of all the postwar Ballets Russes collaborations, but not itself perhaps worthy of the status sometimes accorded it (including by Stravinsky himself) as his first neo-Classical score. *Pulcinella* is a set of arrangements in the manner of Tommasini's Scarlatti ballet *The Good-Humoured Ladies* or the Respighi–Rossini *Boutique fantasque*, both for Diaghilev; and, although Stravinsky's manipulations turn the score into something sharper and more fascinating than the Pergolesi and Gallo originals, they hardly amount to a stylistic revolution. In fact Stravinsky's next work was the *Symphonies of Wind Instruments*, a score as uncompromisingly Russian as anything he ever wrote.

More surprisingly, perhaps, *Pulcinella* was the last ballet Stravinsky composed for Diaghilev, though their association lasted, in its up-and-down way, for another eight years. *Renard*, though premiered by Diaghilev in 1922, was not written for him, and *Les noces*, as we saw, was already composed, though not finally scored, by 1920. After that there was *Apollo* – which Diaghilev adored and made famous in Balanchine's Paris production of 1928, but which was actually written to a commission from the American patroness Elizabeth Sprague Coolidge and premiered at the Library of Congress in Washington earlier that year. Finally, before Diaghilev's death in 1929, there came *The Fairy's Kiss*, written for Ida Rubinstein, a former Diaghilev dancer but now his commercial and artistic rival. For Diaghilev – who had little patience with commerce, paid his debts spasmodically and expected his collaborators to survive otherwise on air – Stravinsky's acceptance of this commission was the ultimate betrayal, and he did not forgive it. In London on different errands in June 1929 they occupied adjacent flats in the same block but neither met nor spoke. Within two months Diaghilev was dead and one of the great artistic collaborations was at an end.

Of these two ballets *Apollo* is unquestionably the masterpiece, a pure embodiment, almost a dramatisation, of the Classical spirit, and astonishingly bold in its disavowal of all the standard Stravinskyisms: the noise, the abrupt discords and hard-edged textures, the drastic rhythmic displacements. In their place: radiant string scoring, elegant melody, a placid discourse of consonance

Victoria Rowell/V&A Images (p22, above left); The Granger Collection/ArenaPAL (p22, below left); Roy Smiljanic/Birmingham Royal Ballet (centre); Bill Cooper/Birmingham Royal Ballet (right)

This ability to do something apparently quite uncharacteristic, and perfect it immediately and on the highest artistic plane, is one of the properties that raises Stravinsky above his contemporaries.

and dissonance, tonal harmony, complete poise and equipoise. This ability to do something apparently quite uncharacteristic, and perfect it immediately and on the highest artistic plane, is one of the properties that raises Stravinsky above his contemporaries. And in a way *The Fairy's Kiss* is another example of the same thing: a kind of *Pulcinella*-ification of piano pieces and songs by Tchaikovsky, it completely transcends what is for the most part minor work and converts it into something compelling and endlessly fascinating, in much the same way (and with comparable techniques) that *Petrushka* transcends its own folk material.

Like its music, the plot of *The Fairy's Kiss* is pure 19th century in origin: a story based on Andersen's *The Ice Maiden*, but plainly indebted in its telling to such archetypal masterpieces as *Giselle* and *Swan Lake*. *Apollo*, on the other hand, is practically storyless, at most a statuesque ceremony devoid of melodrama or conventional narrative interest. This suited the young George Balanchine, whose choreography for Diaghilev played strongly on the abstract forms and formulae of the dance drama, and who ever after showed himself most at home in non-narrative ballets, often based on concert works not written to be danced. In America he choreographed Stravinsky's Violin Concerto (as *Balustrade*) and, under its own name, his *Danses concertantes*. And because the composer respected Balanchine's musicality and enjoyed working with him, he claimed, more than with any other choreographer, his influence is everywhere apparent in Stravinsky's later ballets, even those not composed for him. So *Jeu de cartes*, written in 1936 to a commission from Lincoln Kirstein's American Ballet set up by Balanchine, is again essentially an abstract '19th-century' formulaic ballet, for all its

nominal plot about jokers and straight flushes, while *Orpheus*, which Stravinsky and Balanchine concocted in close collaboration in 1946, bases itself in general outline on the myth, but ceremoniously (like *Apollo*) and largely without anecdotal specifics. On the other hand, *Scènes de ballet*, a 15-minute revue number distantly based on Act 2 of *Giselle* but really about nothing more than two star dancers (Alicia Markova and Anton Dolin) being pursued across the stage by spotlights, was written in some haste in 1944 for the showbiz impresario Billy Rose and staged (after a Philadelphia preview) in Rose's Ziegfeld Theatre in New York as part of his *Seven Lively Arts* show. ▶

Birmingham Royal Ballet's *Card Games*, 2008

Jeu de cartes (1936) Prom 30

First performance Metropolitan Opera House, New York
Company American Ballet
Choreographer George Balanchine
Scenery/Costumes Irene Sharaff

Stravinsky's second US ballet commission was negotiated by George Balanchine on behalf of Lincoln Kirstein's American Ballet company in 1936. There was some debate about the topic, and Stravinsky had already sketched some of the music when he had a brainwave in a taxi cab and came up with the idea of a poker game. In a series of three deals, the Joker (wild card) continuously tricks his way to victory until defeated in the final deal by a royal flush in hearts (love getting the better of evil). As a plot, this is obviously schematic, simply enabling Stravinsky to write a symphonic ballet along Classical lines, with marches, a waltz, a set of solo variations, and a final battle and dance of triumph. Unusually for him, the music includes actual quotations (from Rossini, Ravel, Tchaikovsky and others).

Birmingham Royal Ballet, 2000

Scènes de ballet (1944)
Prom 28

First performance Forrest Theatre, Philadelphia
Choreographer Anton Dolin
Scenery/Costumes Norman Bel Geddes/Paul Dupont

By the 1940s Stravinsky was living in America and staying solvent by accepting commercial projects, including his elephant ballet, *Circus Polka*, and the *Scènes de ballet*, written for Billy Rose's *Seven Lively Arts* revue in 1944. Originally Rose wanted a shortened version of Act 2 of *Giselle* to be danced by Markova, but she objected, and instead Stravinsky was commissioned to write a score 'after' *Giselle*, a prescription he followed very loosely. One can only surmise what Rose's audience thought of this semi-sharp tribute to ballet romanticism, on a ragbag of a bill that included Cole Porter's 'Every time we say goodbye', comedy sketches and a set piece called 'Billy Rose Buys the Metropolitan Opera House'. The work has no noticeable plot, but Stravinsky's music, as ever, is immaculate and hits its target on the nose.

BUT THE REAL BEAUTY OF LUCERNE IS ABBADO, BOULEZ, HAITINK, HERREWEGHE, JANSONS, PAPPANO, RATTLE ....

LUCERNE FESTIVAL IN SUMMER

12 August – 19 September, 2009

www.lucernefestival.ch

LUZERN +
THE CITY. THE LAKE. THE MOUNTAINS.

www.luzern.com

Stravinsky in Paris, 1962

Perhaps Stravinsky and Balanchine's very best work in this genre, though, is their last (apart from the television spectacular *The Flood*). *Agon* was commissioned by Kirstein in 1953 as a companion piece to *Apollo* and *Orpheus*, and he expected another ballet on a classical subject – perhaps from the *Odyssey*. But Stravinsky had once again moved on and was now more interested in numbers and geometry than Greek gods or heroes. Balanchine had had an idea for a time-travelling scenario in which a 16th-century pageant 'took fire in the 20th century and exploded', and this extraordinary idea still survives in the music Stravinsky wrote, which explores material from a 17th-century dance manual by De Lauze but then goes modern in a sequence of short, punchy dances composed according to Stravinsky's version of Schoenberg's 12-tone serial method. The whole ballet is designed as 12 dances performed by 12 dancers clad – in Balanchine's choreography – entirely in practice costume. Thus described, *Agon* sounds like a Constructivist nightmare. In fact it was one of the two or three most brilliant collaborations of Stravinsky's whole career and perhaps the most dazzling illustration of his capacity for self-renewal. At 75 he had produced the most sophisticated, the most elegant and the most up-to-date ballet score anyone could possibly have expected from a composer half his age. After the New York premiere in 1957, the great dance critic Edwin Denby wrote, 'The balcony stood up shouting and whistling when the choreographer took his bow [the composer was not present]. Downstairs, people came out into the lobby, their eyes bright as if the piece had been champagne.' The corks have been popping ever since. ●

Stephen Walsh is the author of a major recent two-volume biography of Stravinsky and holds a Chair in Music at Cardiff University.

Orpheus (1947) Prom 40

First performance City Center of Music and Drama, New York
Company Ballet Society
Choreographer George Balanchine
Scenery/Costumes Isamu Noguchi

Stravinsky's Orpheus ballet, a rather obvious subject, perhaps, for the great neo-Classicist in what seemed to many his declining years, was commissioned by Lincoln Kirstein in 1946 and premiered by Kirstein's Ballet Society in New York in April 1948. The familiar story – Eurydice's death, Orpheus's descent to Hades, his turning to look at her as they reascend, and his dismemberment by the Furies – is told in outline, but so ritualised (by Balanchine and the composer working together) as to convert its narrative into a kind of mobile sculpture. Similarly the score, superficially neo-Classical in tone, texture and form, contains mysterious austerities that reflect Stravinsky's growing interest in a more ancient and intricate music, that of Bach and much earlier. *Orpheus* is one of Stravinsky's least-known masterpieces, but a masterpiece nonetheless.

Costume design by Gerd Hartung, Deutsche Oper Berlin, 1990.

Agon (1957) Prom 57

First performance City Center of Music and Drama, New York
Company New York City Ballet
Choreographer George Balanchine

After *Orpheus*, Lincoln Kirstein nagged Stravinsky for a third ballet to make a classical triptych (with *Apollo*), and eventually the composer obliged with *Agon*, a plotless, abstract ballet based in various ways on the number 12 and partly employing his latest obsession, 12-note serialism. Work on *Agon* began late in 1953, but was interrupted by the *Canticum sacrum* (a Venice Biennale commission) and completed only in 1957. Kirstein's production, choreographed by Balanchine with the dancers in black-and-white rehearsal kit, opened at the end of that year. Descriptions of *Agon* can make it sound mechanical, but it is the reverse, constantly alive from start to finish, including some of the most brilliant 17th-century dance recreations (sarabande, galliard, bourrée) in any modern work, and the most stunning of musical transformations in its closing pages.

New York City Ballet, 1952

Title-image: Mara Galeazzi as The Chosen One, *The Rite of Spring*, Royal Ballet, 2008

Stephen Jackson Director

Join the BBC Symphony Chorus

The BBC Symphony Chorus, currently celebrating its 80th anniversary, is one of the finest and most distinctive amateur choirs in the UK. In its appearances with the BBC Symphony Orchestra, the Chorus undertakes a wide range of challenging repertoire which is usually broadcast on BBC Radio 3. This season's concerts with the BBC SO have included Beethoven's *Missa solemnis* and Bruckner's Mass in F minor, both conducted by Jiří Bělohlávek, Orff's *Carmina burana*, Poulenc's *Stabat Mater* and a solo concert in LSO St Luke's conducted by Chorus Director Stephen Jackson and featuring music by Poulenc, Turnage and Vivancos.

As resident chorus for the BBC Proms, the Symphony Chorus takes part in five or six concerts each season, including the Last Night. This year's Proms performances include Bruckner's Psalm 150 and Brahms's *Alto Rhapsody*, both conducted by Jiří Bělohlávek, Szymanowski's *Stabat Mater* conducted by Osma Vänskä, Berlioz's *Te Deum* conducted by Susanna Mälkki, Holst's *First Choral Symphony* with the BBC National Orchestra of Wales and Philip Glass's Symphony No. 7 with the BBC Scottish Symphony Orchestra.

2009–10 Season Highlights

As part of the BBC Symphony Orchestra's 2009–10 Barbican season, the BBC Symphony Chorus will perform works including:

Brahms
A German Requiem

Josquin des Prez
Nymphes des bois

Hans Werner Henze
Elogium musicum

Ian McQueen
Earthly Paradise

Would you like to join us?

Do you love singing? Do you want to make music at the highest level with great conductors and orchestras? Would you like to work on new and challenging repertoire, as well as standard choral works, with a dynamic chorus director and lively sociable singers? If the answer's 'yes', then the BBC Symphony Chorus is the choir for you! Membership is free and includes individual vocal training. New members are always welcome to apply.

To find out more,
visit **bbc.co.uk/symphonychorus**
or contact Emma Cotsell,
Administrator, BBC Symphony Chorus,
BBC Maida Vale Studios,
Delaware Road,
London W9 2LG

emma.cotsell@bbc.co.uk
020 7765 4715

BBC RADIO 3
90–93FM

STUDY at the
Royal College of Music

· **Teachers** of international repute, accustomed to unlocking the potential of the most gifted musicians.

· Plenty of **opportunities to perform** at the highest level as a soloist or in ensemble.

· An **environment** that nurtures and challenges, an **atmosphere** rich in artistic stimulus, and the best **practical resources** that reflect and serve your ambition.

· A **location** at the heart of a city with a cultural life that is unsurpassed anywhere in the world.

Visit **www.rcm.ac.uk/studying** to find out more, or drop in and pick up a copy of our latest prospectus

RCM LONDON

Royal College of Music, Prince Consort Road, London SW7

LISTEN at the
Royal College of Music

· **Opera productions** featuring some of the stars of tomorrow, by the leading directors of today

· Thrilling **orchestral concerts** under conductors such as Bernard Haitink, Sir Roger Norrington, Andrew Litton, Vladimir Jurowski and John Wilson

· **Chamber concerts, solo performances** and **song recitals** from international prize-winners

· **Early music** performances on instruments from the RCM's unique collection; **new music** festivals with today's leading composers

Visit **www.rcm.ac.uk/events** to find out more, or drop in and pick up a copy of our latest events guide

RCM LONDON

Royal College of Music, Prince Consort Road, London SW7

COMPOSERS
OF THE YEAR

PURCELL · HANDEL · HAYDN · MENDELSSOHN

As **BBC Radio 3 continues**
its year-long celebration of
anniversary composers **Purcell,
Handel, Haydn and Mendelssohn,**
Richard Wigmore considers their
far-reaching influence, and
introduces some of their key
works appearing at the Proms

HAYDN...

Henry Purcell (1659–95)
'the delight of the Nation and the Wonder of the World'

Even in his brief, hectic lifetime Henry Purcell was acknowledged as the greatest living English composer. After his death aged only 36, he was hailed 'the Delight of the Nation and the Wonder of the World'; a century later he had become 'our musical Shakespeare'. None of his contemporaries matched his melodic genius, his versatility or his inspired eclecticism, which drew on the latest French and Italian styles without sacrificing a quintessential Englishness. His sensitivity to the rhythms and cadences of the English language remains unsurpassed.

Until the late 1680s Purcell's activities centred on court and chapel, with the production of verse anthems, royal odes and welcome songs (in which the music repeatedly transcends the toe-curlingly sycophantic texts), and, in 1685, coronation anthems for James II. After the 'Bloodless' Revolution the pattern of Purcell's creative life changed. He continued to provide occasional odes for the new royal family but, with the militaristic William III opposed to elaborate church music, he now began to compose for a broader, less refined middle-class audience: in the published sets of 'choyce ayres and songs', in incidental music for plays (including the tragedy *Abdelazar*) and in the so-called 'semi-operas' for the Dorset Garden Theatre, off Fleet Street. Purcell the court composer had morphed into Purcell the composer for the commercial stage. All-sung opera was still deemed alien to the English temperament. The recipe for public success was to take an existing play, fillet it and stuff it with music, dance and spectacular scenic effects. These multimedia Restoration extravaganzas, involving separate casts of actors, dancers and singers, present a serious challenge to today's opera producers. Yet the four semi-operas, from Purcell's final years – *Dioclesian*, *King Arthur*, *The Fairy Queen* and *The Indian Queen* – contain some of his most thrilling, atmospheric and melodically alluring music.

Henry Purcell
The Fairy Queen

In an era of extravagant theatrical entertainments *The Fairy Queen* outdid all the competition. The staging, in London's Dorset Garden Theatre in May 1692, cost an outlandish £3,000 and involved a cast of 40 singers, actors and dancers, fantastic scenic effects (including swans transformed into fairies and a garden of gushing fountains) and dancing monkeys. Purcell's series of fairy masques had only a tangential connection with the play proper, an abridged and 'modernised' version of *A Midsummer Night's Dream* (Restoration audiences could not cope with undiluted Shakespeare). But the music is gloriously inventive, ranging from the fairies' taunting of the stuttering Drunken Poet in Act 1 and the hilarious rustic courtship of Coridon and Mopsa, to the ravishing invocations to sleep in Act 2, with their quintessentially Purcellian voluptuous melancholy.

George Frideric Handel (1685–1759)
'the Orpheus of our century'

Trained in the Lutheran contrapuntal tradition of his native Saxony, Handel honed his command of form and fluid, long-arched melody during a glittering three-year sojourn in Italy. After settling in England in 1712 he quickly became the *de facto* resident composer of the Haymarket opera company, and a court 'insider'. Long before he took English citizenship in 1727, the year of the resplendent Coronation anthems for George II, he was being acclaimed as 'the Orpheus of our Century', the inheritor of Purcell's mantle as Britain's national composer.

Like his great predecessor, Handel was a born theatre animal. But, whereas Purcell lavished his genius on hybrid entertainments, Handel took advantage of the new craze among the nobility for all-sung Italian opera. Nay-sayers derided this exotic foreign import, with its temperamental and vastly expensive prima donnas and castratos, but London's elite was undeterred, and for over two decades from 1719 Handel devoted his chief creative energies to operas for the Royal Academy company. Many are in lofty heroic vein, others belong to a category of 'magic operas', while works such as *Partenope* and *Xerxes* mine a delightful seam of satirical comedy.

It was only in 1741, with the Academy virtually bankrupt, that Handel finally abandoned Italian opera for English oratorio. The Scriptures-based *Messiah*, premiered in Dublin in April 1742, was a unique case. The other oratorios – including *Saul*, *Samson*, *Solomon* and *Jephtha* – were unstaged dramas, designed for a puritanically inclined middle-class audience during Lent. Typically they drew on Old Testament stories with ▶

I WAS CUT OFF FROM THE WORLD AND FORCED TO BECOME ORIGINAL

STURM UND DRANG!

HAYDN...

Handel
Partenope; Samson

Partenope was a controversial and, as it proved, unpopular choice with London audiences accustomed to operas on heroic dynastic themes. One theatre agent even thought that the plot, centring on the amorous entanglements of the Neapolitan Queen Partenope, would encourage 'depravity of Taste'. To us now it appears as one of Handel's most delightful operas: a witty yet humane exposé of lovers' foibles that pokes fun at the conventions of *opera seria*. The flighty Queen, wilfully manipulating her gaggle of admirers, is an irresistible Handelian creation, her character epitomised in the kittenish minuet aria 'Qual farfalletta'.

If *Partenope* was a virtual failure, *Samson*, premiered at Covent Garden in February 1743, scored an immediate and enduring success. The acerbic Horace Walpole, a diehard supporter of Italian opera, derided the predominantly English cast ('a man with one note in his voice, and a girl without ever an one'). But Handel and his new oratorio public valued dramatic truth above vocal virtuosity. With its epic theme and vividly drawn contrasts between nations and individuals – the blind hero pitted against his cooing, coquettish wife Dalila and the Philistine heavy Harapha – *Samson* is the archetypal Handelian oratorio, setting the pattern for the great biblical dramas of his final creative years.

contemporary political and religious resonances. In two seasons Handel varied the mix with dramas drawn from Greek mythology, *Semele* and *Hercules*. Castigated as 'a bawdy opera', *Semele* flopped with audiences expecting Lenten edification. Yet, in an age that no longer blurs morality and aesthetic worth, this delectable tragicomedy of lust and overweening ambition has rightly become one of Handel's best-loved works.

Joseph Haydn (1732–1809)
'a universal genius'

By the late 1780s, more famous internationally than any composer had been in his own lifetime, Haydn had come to resent his secluded existence as Kapellmeister to the Hungarian Esterházy family. Luckily for him, Prince Nikolaus Esterházy's death in 1790 freed him to sign a lucrative contract with the violinist and impresario Johann Peter Salomon, with whom he travelled to London for the first of two highly successful visits.

Here Haydn was immediately hailed as 'a universal genius' and lionised as a cultural hero; and he scored

Haydn
The Creation; The Seven Last Words of Our Saviour on the Cross

'Perhaps the most sublime composition without words to point out its meaning' was the music historian Charles Burney's verdict on Haydn's *The Seven Last Words*, a series of orchestral meditations commissioned by a canon of Cadiz around 1786. Today this lofty, fervently Catholic music is more often heard in Haydn's arrangement for string quartet, and in the oratorio version of 1796. The success of the premiere enhanced Haydn's reputation as a choral composer, and fuelled Viennese anticipation for *The Creation*.

The public premiere of *The Creation* in March 1799 capped even Haydn's London triumphs. The music's effortless fusion of melodic charm, pictorialism and elemental grandeur carried instant appeal and Haydn's joyous celebration of an ordered, enlightened universe was soon being performed throughout the German-speaking lands, as well as in France and in Britain.

a series of unalloyed triumphs with the two contracted sets of 'London' symphonies, Nos. 93–98 and 99–104. These are Haydn's most flamboyant, worldly symphonies, reflecting the exhilarating milieu in which they were written, but also his most profound and intently argued. The musically sophisticated London audiences were evidently prepared to be challenged as well as entertained.

In London, too, Haydn made his crucial encounter with the music of Handel. Profoundly stirred by monster performances of *Messiah* and *Israel in Egypt* in Westminster Abbey in 1791, he was immediately fired by the idea of composing an oratorio of his own. But it was only after his final return to Vienna in 1795 that he embarked on *The Creation*, perhaps his supreme achievement. Mingling Handelian contrapuntal splendour with Haydn's own orchestral mastery, harmonic daring and pastoral lyricism, *The Creation* set the final seal on Haydn's fame, and quickly became a national cultural monument, as *Messiah* had long been in Britain.

Felix Mendelssohn (1809–47)
'the Mozart of the 19th century'

More than 150 years after his death, aged just 38, Felix Mendelssohn is still too often treated with faint condescension, as if we cannot forgive him for the affluence and adulation he enjoyed in his lifetime. As music's most precocious genius – more, even, than Mozart – he produced a stream of dazzlingly original works in his teens. In 1825 came the Octet, unequalled in its mix of youthful exuberance and compositional sophistication. A year later he conjured shimmering new sonorities in his *A Midsummer Night's Dream* overture. A visit to Scotland in 1829 inspired the overture *The Hebrides*, praised by Wagner as 'the masterpiece of a landscape painter of the first order'. ▶

Mark Thomas/BBC

STEINWAY & SONS

BEFORE A MAJOR CONCERT, THE WORLD'S FINEST PIANISTS SEE WORDS OF REASSURANCE

The fact that most major pianists and venues in the world choose Steinway is breathtaking. Yet the reason for our success is quite simple. In a mass produced and price conscious world, Steinway has not compromised. Each Steinway piano owes its unique characteristics and incomparable sound to the people who carefully and individually create it. Suffice to say that those at the very top of their profession, as well as those who simply want the best, invest in nothing less.

STEINWAY HALL   44 MARYLEBONE LANE   LONDON W1U 2DB

020 7487 3391
www.steinway.co.uk

RSC
ROYAL
SHAKESPEARE
COMPANY

RSC ENSEMBLE
2009-2011

Image created by RSC Graphic Design, original painting Alfred Sisley.

SELECT YOUR OWN SEAT ONLINE
www.rsc.org.uk
(NO BOOKING FEE)

RSC TICKET HOTLINE
0844 800 1110
(NO BOOKING FEE, CALLS FROM
BT LANDLINE COST 5P PER MINUTE)

STRATFORD-UPON-AVON
MARCH—OCTOBER
09

THE WINTER'S TALE
FROM 31 MARCH 09 WILLIAM SHAKESPEARE

AS YOU LIKE IT
FROM 18 APRIL 09 WILLIAM SHAKESPEARE

JULIUS CAESAR
FROM 15 MAY 09 WILLIAM SHAKESPEARE

THE DRUNKS
FROM 21 AUGUST 09 MIKHAIL AND VYACHESLAV DURNENKOV

THE GRAIN STORE
FROM 10 SEPTEMBER 09 NATAL'IA VOROZHBIT

accenture
High performance. Delivered.

ARTS COUNCIL
ENGLAND

Incurably restless by temperament, Mendelssohn lived his adult life at a feverish pace, as composer, virtuoso pianist, organist and a conductor who brought a new energy and precision to the art. Like Handel and Haydn before him, he was idolised in England, by both the public and the royal family. In 1842 he dedicated his 'Scottish' Symphony to the young Queen Victoria.

More than any of his contemporaries, Mendelssohn set a premium on lucidity, grace and fastidious craftsmanship. Not for nothing did Schumann call him 'the Mozart of the 19th century'. He retained a lifelong reverence for the music of Handel (*Elijah* is the 19th century's most successful example of a neo-Handelian oratorio) and, especially, Bach, whose *St Matthew Passion* he famously revived in 1829.

Yet, for all his Classical and Baroque sympathies, Mendelssohn also possessed a true Romantic sensibility, with a genius for the picturesque and the fanciful. His two most famous symphonies, the 'Scottish' and the 'Italian', are a quintessentially Romantic fusion of the musical and the visual. And the equally Romantic *A Midsummer Night's Dream* music is just one of several late works (the ever-fresh Violin Concerto is another) to challenge the old saw that Mendelssohn's inspiration declined irrevocably after the brilliance of youth. ●

For more information on BBC Radio 3's Composers of the Year broadcasts throughout 2009 – including Handel's complete operas and Haydn complete symphonies, visit bbc.co.uk/composers

Mark Thomas/BBC

Mendelssohn
The five symphonies

More than any of his contemporaries, Mendelssohn achieved a vital, creative fusion of Classical forms and Romantic expression. Although he eschewed programmatic titles, his two most famous symphonies, the 'Scottish' (No. 3) and the 'Italian' (No. 4, whose spontaneous exuberance belies its protracted genesis), were a response to landscape and history. Both reveal a painter's genius for colour and perspective: in the brilliant Mediterranean light of the 'Italian' Symphony's first movement, the sense of a procession receding into the distance in the Andante, or the subtle chiaroscuro of the 'Scottish' Symphony's misty opening, inspired by the mouldering, ivy-clad ruins of Queen Mary's chapel at Holyrood.

Mendelssohn had cut his teeth as a symphonist with 12 string symphonies of 1821–3 but the first symphony he saw fit to publish was the C minor, composed around his 15th birthday. This precociously assured work mingles half-echoes of Mozart's great G minor Symphony (No. 40) with many piquant individual touches. Mendelssohn's other two symphonies celebrate the Lutheran faith into which he had been baptised: the symphony-cantata 'Lobgesang' (Hymn of Praise, No. 2), a favourite in Victorian England, and the 'Reformation', composed for the tercentenary of the 1530 Augsburg Confession, and culminating in a triumphant burst of the Lutheran chorale 'Ein' feste Burg ist unser Gott'.

Richard Wigmore is a writer, broadcaster and lecturer specialising in the Viennese Classical period. His 'Pocket Guide to Haydn' (Faber) was published in January.

Composers of the Year at the Proms

Purcell
Abdelazar – suite
Prom 53, 25 August
Arias and duets
PCM 14, 30 August
Chacony (arr. Britten)
PCM 4, 10 August
Dido and Aeneas – excerpts;
Purcell Suite (arr. Henry Wood)
Prom 76, 12 September
Evening Hymn, songs, *etc.*
PCM 19, 7 September
The Fairy Queen
Prom 7, 21 July

Handel
Arias
PCM 14, 30 August
Messiah
Prom 68, 6 September
Music for the Royal Fireworks – excerpts
Prom 76, 12 September
Partenope
Prom 4, 19 July
Samson
Prom 47, 20 August
Solomon – The Arrival of the Queen of Sheba; Four Coronation Anthems; Semele – excerpts; Motet 'Salve Regina'; Organ Concerto, Op. 4 No. 4
Prom 36, 12 August
Xerxes – 'Ombra mai fu'; Alcina – 'Ah, mio cor!'; Water Music – Suite No. 2
Prom 53, 25 August

Haydn
Arias and canzonettas
PCM 14, 30 August
The Creation
Prom 2, 18 July
Scena di Berenice
Prom 53, 25 August
The Seven Last Words of Our Saviour on the Cross
Prom 6, 20 July

String Quartet in D major, Op. 20 No. 4
PCM 11, 30 August
String Quartet in F sharp minor, Op. 50 No. 4
PCM 3, 3 August
String Quartet in G major, Op. 77 No. 1
PCM 7, 29 August
Symphony No. 97
Prom 73, 10 September
Symphony No. 100, 'Military'
Prom 62, 1 September
Symphony No. 101, 'Clock'
Prom 51, 23 August
Trumpet Concerto
Prom 76, 12 September

Mendelssohn
A Midsummer Night's Dream – excerpts
Prom 72, 9 September
Octet
Prom 49, 21 August
Overture 'The Hebrides'
Prom 70, 8 September
Piano Concerto No. 1
Prom 69, 7 September
Piano Trio in D minor, Op. 49
PCM 6, 24 August
Piano Trio in C minor, Op. 66
PCM 14, 30 August
Prelude and Fugue in E minor, Op. 35 No. 1
PCM 5, 17 August
Songs Without Words – selection
PCM 15, 31 August
Symphony No. 1; Violin Concerto
Prom 26, 4 August
Symphony No. 2, 'Lobgesang'
Prom 19, 30 July
Symphony No. 3, 'Scottish'
Prom 53, 25 August
Symphony No. 4, 'Italian'
Prom 29, 6 August
Symphony No. 5, 'Reformation'
Prom 20, 31 July

Step into new musical worlds with the BBC Singers

Visit **bbc.co.uk/singers** for details

BBC RADIO 3

90 – 93 FM

What BBT means to me

guidance

Christianne Stotijn

encouragement

Christian Poltéra

family

Emma Bell

dreams

Antoine Tamestit

realisation

Colin Currie

generosity

Jonathan Biss

The generosity of the BB Trust goes far beyond the financial – it is about nurturing a love for music, and giving musicians the support and the space to become better ones. *Jonathan Biss*

1934: ENGLAND AT THE CROSSROADS

For many, the deaths of Elgar, Holst and Delius 75 years ago represented the end of an era. Stephen Johnson looks at how, with the births of Harrison Birtwistle and Peter Maxwell Davies, 1934 became a turning point in the landscape of British music

There are dates around which significant events cluster like planets around a giant star. Sometimes there's a clear historical reason; for others the cause is mysterious, like one of those infuriating motorway traffic jams that seem simply to have appeared out of nowhere. It's hard to put a finger on exactly why 1934 marks such a turning point in British music. But for a start there were two epochal symphonic premieres – Vaughan Williams's Fourth and Walton's First – each of which radically altered its composer's public profile; and, if Elgar had lived to complete his Third Symphony that same year, there would almost certainly have been another.

Elgar's death on 23 February – duly mourned as it was at the time – seemed even more fateful when it was quickly followed by those of Gustav Holst (25 May) and Frederick Delius (10 June). Here were three very different composers – interestingly each of them beyond the apex of his reputation. Elgar, though still honoured as the founding father of the 20th-century British musical renaissance, had been out of fashion since the end of the First World War. Perhaps the reminders in his music of what he himself had called Edwardian England's 'glad

Holst (*left*) with Elgar during the 1920s

Shutterstock (page 36): ArenaPAL (above left): akg-images (below right)

as the composer put it, is haunted by a 'malign influence'. The return of this tortuously chromatic theme on massed brass and percussion at the height of the third movement is a passage that can still startle people who think they have Elgar safely pigeonholed. At the symphony's premiere one critic heard 'pessimism and rebellion' in this music. It's certainly the most complete self-portrait this complex, tortured artist ever penned, and – even if it is with hindsight – it's hard not to infer that the crisis it expresses is more than personal.

Two works by Delius also reveal very different sides of their creator. For some the 'English Rhapsody' *Brigg Fair* (1907) will do nothing but confirm the received impression of this composer. Lush, nostalgic, haunted by a gently melancholic folk tune, it can easily be dismissed as Arcadian escapism. In fact it's much more than that, its pathos surely deriving in part from Delius's very adult realisation that the vision is impossible. But *Song of the High Hills* (begun in 1911, the same year as Elgar completed his Second Symphony) is still more original. Scored for a very large, colour-enhanced orchestra (including three timpanists) and wordless chorus, it turns its back completely on purposeful, symphonic development. Ideas float into one another like images in a dream. There is no sense of journeying to a finally achieved destination – only moments of fleeting drama and beauty, like changing cloudscapes.

Just as striking is the contrast offered by the two big Holst works featured this season. Throughout Holst's later career, *The Planets* (1914–16) was his one supreme hit, eclipsing almost everything else he wrote. For that reason some self-conscious sophisticates still dismiss it. More fool them: *The Planets* is one of the most original, imaginative and technically brilliant things in the British orchestral repertoire. The same scintillating inventive intelligence can be found at work in the Keats-inspired *First Choral Symphony* (1923–4; alas there was no Second), but instead of the extroversion of *The Planets* one senses a mind turned inward, surpassing even the delicious mysticism of the earlier work's concluding 'Neptune'. Even the puckish humour of the Scherzo 'Fancy' evaporates mysteriously, while the setting of Keats's famous 'Ode on a Grecian Urn' enriches and extends the familiar language of tonality in a weirdly atmospheric evocation of the poem's 'Cold Pastoral'. Audiences and critics in Holst's time were generally baffled or dismissive. Today's Proms audiences should be able to do it much more justice. Before ▶

confident morning' were just too poignant to a country that had lost so much, and too embarrassing for a generation of younger composers anxious to forget the past and keen to push forwards. Elgar's creative near-silence after the Cello Concerto (1919) had only added to the feeling in some quarters that he was yesterday's man.

For those who like to uncover a historical 'narrative' in a composer's output, the Elgar works included in this Proms season are a gift. Elgar's breakthrough piece – still one of his most popular – the *Enigma Variations* (1899) features in the final concert of the '1934 weekend' (25–26 July), alongside important works by Delius and Holst. Abundant Edwardian vigour and confidence sing out in the *Pomp and Circumstance* March No. 4 (1907 – including a tune almost as great as 'Land of Hope and Glory' from the March No. 1) and the warm, vivid London portrait *Cockaigne* (1900–01). Then there's the opulent, splendidly assured 'concert overture' *In the South (Alassio)* of 1904, opening with a clear tribute to the leading continental modernist of the time, Richard Strauss. On the other hand the *Severn Suite* (1930, originally for brass band, but later arranged by Elgar's friend Ivor Atkins as the Organ Sonata No. 2), fine as it is, suggests a composer defiantly refusing to march with progress. The key Elgar work, however, is the Second Symphony (1909–11). At first airborne and optimistic, the first movement soon shows us a very different side of the composer – and perhaps of his time and place: the 'garden',

Delius

Sir Peter Maxwell Davies (*left*) with Sir Harrison Birtwistle in Lucerne, 2004

leaving English pastoralism – cold or otherwise – one other rare inclusion is well worth noting. E. J. Moeran began his Symphony in G minor in 1934. Like Elgar's *Severn Suite* it seems irredeemably anachronistic: easy to dismiss as a blend of English folksy nostalgia and pre-war 'Celtic Twilight', plus some rather obvious invocations to Sibelius. But its freshness, lyrical appeal and atmospheric richness make labels like 'reactionary' or 'derivative' seem trivial and irrelevant. It remains at core an authentic, haunting piece, and its revival at the Proms deserves a big welcome.

Apart from three significant deaths, 1934 saw two equally significant births: Harrison Birtwistle and Peter Maxwell Davies. In his gleefully provocative youth, Maxwell Davies happily dismissed composers such as Delius and even Holst for 'dancing on the village green' while the real Continental greats – Schoenberg, Webern, Stravinsky, Bartók – were bravely exploring hitherto uncharted regions. Then – gradually – his view began to change. The first milestone was his public admission, in the early 1980s, of a debt to Sibelius. This coincided with his discovery of the Orkney Islands,

one of which, Hoy, was to become his home and inspiration for many years. Prom 70 (8 September) celebrates this neatly by placing the UK premiere of his Violin Concerto No. 2, written for the dynamic Daniel Hope, in between Sibelius's Fifth Symphony (whose musical currents and undercurrents have been a powerful influence on Maxwell Davies's later style) and Mendelssohn's *The Hebrides* overture – not quite the Orkneys, but close enough for comparisons to flow freely. And in the Late Night Prom that same evening the BBC Singers performs two of his Far-North-inspired choral pieces: *Westerlings* and the atmospheric *Solstice of Light* for chorus and organ.

Like Maxwell Davies, the young Harrison Birtwistle found himself (more reluctantly perhaps) being cheered on by the kind of card-carrying modernists who thought that the country would be a better place if only it could forget the likes of Elgar, Delius and Holst. So Birtwistle's calm admission, during a Radio 3 festival of his music in the mid-1980s, that the musical landscapes of Holst and Vaughan Williams were a formative influence on his own style had something of the shock effect of a public 'coming-out'. Still, the brooding elemental quality of Birtwistle's *Silbury Air* (1977) can be related to Holst's *Egdon Heath* or the 'Landscape' movement from Vaughan Williams's *Sinfonia antartica*, while the ritualised, non-developmental 'progress' of *Verses for Ensembles* (1968–9) and *Carmen arcadiae mechanicae perpetuum* (1977) surely owes as much to the example of Holst as to Stravinsky – the slow-moving processionals in Holst's *First Choral Symphony* find echo again and again in Birtwistle's work. Yet in the face of something as engrossing and startlingly original as Act 2 of Birtwistle's opera *The Mask of Orpheus* (completed 1984) the urge to play 'compare and contrast' quickly vanishes. Orpheus's descent into Hades in his archetypally doomed attempt to rescue his wife Euridice becomes a teeming, roaring, emotionally convulsive musical white-water ride – terrifying yet cathartic. ●

Stephen Johnson has written regularly for *The Independent*, *The Guardian* and *BBC Music Magazine*, and is the author of books on Bruckner, Mahler and Wagner. He is a regular presenter of BBC Radio 3's *Discovering Music* (Sundays, 5.00pm).

1934: England at the Crossroads

The Orkney island of Hoy

Elgar
Cockaigne
Prom 12, 25 July

Enigma Variations
Prom 14, 26 July

In the South (Alassio)
Prom 1, 17 July

Organ Sonatas Nos. 1 & 2
Prom 11, 25 July

Pomp and Circumstance
March No. 1
Prom 76, 12 September

Pomp and Circumstance
March No. 4
Prom 13, 26 July

Symphony No. 2
Prom 9, 23 July

Violin Sonata
PCM 10, 29 August

Delius
Brigg Fair
Prom 14, 26 July

Cello Sonata
PCM 10, 29 August

On Hearing the First
Cuckoo in Spring
Proms 21 & 23, 1 & 2 August

The Song of the High Hills
Prom 12, 25 July

Holst
First Choral Symphony
Prom 14, 26 July

Four Songs, Op. 35;
Six Songs, Op. 15 – selection
PCM 10, 29 August

The Planets
Prom 12, 25 July

A Song of the Night
Prom 13, 26 July

Maxwell Davies
Roma amor
Prom 29, 6 August

Solstice of Light; Westerlings
Prom 71, 8 September

Violin Concerto No. 2
Prom 70, 8 September

Birtwistle
Carmen arcadiae mechanicae
perpetuum; Silbury Air;
Verses for Ensembles
Prom 27, 4 August

The Mask of Orpheus –
The Arches
Prom 39, 14 August

Betty Freeman/Lebrecht Music & Arts (below left); Doug Houghton Photography (above right)

going
100s of auctions monthly

going
bid anywhere, any time

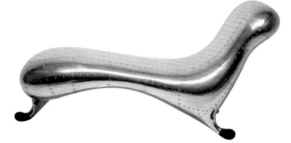

gone
fastest-growing free auction database

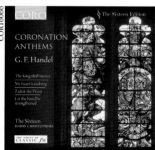
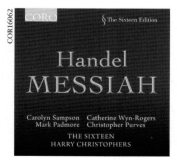

PASSIONS IGNITED
AT THE PIANO

Stephen Hough – the first soloist to perform Tchaikovsky's complete piano-and-orchestra works in a single Proms season – offers his pianist's-eye-view of these pieces, as he limbers up for the challenge ahead

Tchaikovsky's four works for piano and orchestra are a strangely diverse cycle. They feature one of the most famous concertos ever written (No. 1); one of the most unjustly neglected concertos ever written (No. 2); a one-movement piece that began life as a symphony – not really a concerto at all (No. 3); and the two-movement Concert Fantasia, which escaped being called a concerto altogether.

Unlike Rachmaninov's hand-in-glove pianism – where perfectly fitting note-patterns seem smoothly stitched around every finger – Tchaikovsky's piano-writing feels more like unhewn blocks grasped in a sculptor's stone-scarred paw. The chords are awkward and jagged, arpeggios tumble around the thumbs in ungrateful shards; passagework that works well in the right hand is doled out in unison for both hands, the left hand in danger of dragging along as an ungainly companion. Even the glorious melodies (and what a cup-running-over there is in these works) are often supported by bottom-heavy accompaniment – the right hand's fifth finger striving to make itself heard above the harmonic storm. But never mind the physical dangers. The musical journey is so often traversed along an emotional tightrope, with lions of hysteria or bombast below; yet in a successful performance you reach the other side unscathed, if not unaffected. The balancing pole is the innocence that is at the heart of all Tchaikovsky's music – a longing for childhood, a wistful delight in a fantasy world. It is the acute sensitivity with which he juxtaposes powerful, poignant adult emotions with this purity of youth that, for me, makes his music so uniquely touching.

Tchaikovsky was not a pianist – a fact that hardly seems significant until we realise that most other composers who wrote piano concertos before (or after) him were usually good enough to play their solo parts themselves. This fact not only affected the way Tchaikovsky wrote for the piano, but it endangered the very existence, or integrity, of these works. Three different pianists were solicited for comments on the three numbered concertos at the time of their writing, and each of them failed to appreciate or fully understand the composer's work. It's no wonder that Tchaikovsky became prone to bouts of deep self-doubt.

Famously, the Piano Concerto No. 1 (1874–5) was dismissed by Nikolay Rubinstein, its intended dedicatee, as 'banal, clumsy and incompetently written'. Indeed, he deemed it 'unplayable'. The Second Concerto (1879–80) was offered to Alexander Siloti for comments and, instead of making some small adjustments, he responded by deleting over half of the second movement. This mutilation, abhorred by the composer, was nevertheless published and remained the version most

Alexander Siloti (*left*) with Tchaikovsky. Siloti's mutilated version of Tchaikovsky's Second Piano Concerto remained popular with pianists well into the 20th century

The musical journey is so often traversed along an emotional tightrope ... The balancing pole is the innocence that is at the heart of Tchaikovsky's music – a longing for childhood, a wistful delight in a fantasy world.

performed until late last century. The Third Concerto (1893), Tchaikovsky's last work – originally meant to be a symphony – is a more complex case, as only the first movement was actually completed, and it was not published until after the composer's death. Sergey Taneyev, the pianist approached this time for practical advice, was lukewarm about the piece, leading Tchaikovsky to threaten to destroy it. Only the Concert Fantasia, composed nine years earlier, seems to have offended no-one, but it has ended up being the least performed of the four concertante works.

The opening of the First Concerto is a curiosity. Firstly, it is in the wrong key: after the first four notes, the slashing orchestral chords swerve instantly from B flat minor to its relative major – and into those famous bounding opening piano chords. Secondly, the musical material of this introduction, stirring and inspired as it is, never appears again in the rest of the work; it is a rare example of a substantial concerto opening section that bears no relationship to what follows. Musicologists can always find unlikely and unintended connections between thematic material and fragments across a piece but, with the best will in the world, it is impossible to make any connections here.

The Second Concerto starts without an introduction and in a firmly centred home key. Its quirks are the presence of three cadenzas in the first movement, and the prominence of the solo violin and cello in the second. This latter movement was a cause of controversy at the first performance, both because of its length and because of the lack of presence of the solo piano, and there are two passages which the composer himself suggested cutting. As a latter-day acolyte of the composer, I (tentatively, respectfully) think I might have found the solution that eluded Siloti and his over-sharp red pencil. The second sanctioned cut, right at the end of the movement, is one of my favourite moments in the concerto. I am sure I could convince the self-doubting composer that it has to stay, and that it is utterly ▶

Lebrecht Music & Arts/Shutterstock (p42 illustration); Grant Hiroshima (p42 Hough); ArenaPAL (right)

Galatea and Pygmalion (*left and right*) – subjects of the impromptu ballet which Tchaikovsky danced with Saint-Saëns in Moscow during the latter's visit in 1876

is called upon to bear, including its extravagant cadenza, which contains possibly the longest trill in the entire concerto repertoire. (Having mentioned Saint-Saëns, I can't resist thinking of the incident when, during his visit to Tchaikovsky in 1876, the two composers danced an improvised ballet on the main stage of the Moscow Conservatory. Nikolay Rubinstein was the pianist for this picturesque, but mercifully private, performance.)

It is extraordinary to learn that the Concert Fantasia was performed quite often in the years after its creation, because today it is the least known of the cycle. At the time it was written, such concert pieces for soloist and orchestra appeared frequently on the potpourri, mixed-bill concert programmes then in fashion. Being cast in two movements probably precluded this piece from being called a concerto, and the movements are strangely titled. The first is *Quasi rondo* – strange, because it is formally nothing of the sort, unless a vague resemblance to lively finale movements was in the composer's mind. The second movement, entitled *Contrastes*, is really a slow movement followed without a break by a fast movement – a contrast indeed but, despite the return of material from the slow section, perhaps not one that would naturally lend itself to such a title.

lovely if played with complete conviction by soloist and orchestra. The other cut occurs at a moment when the structure does appear uneasy, but this has to do not with excessive length but with an imbalance of solo instrumental prominence. It is a glorious tune, which we have already heard early in the movement played by the solo violin and cello. But at this later point – as it expands, intensifies, and then unfolds into the piano cadenza's rolled chords – it simply needs to be played by the piano, rather than the solo stringed instruments again. So here I have 'reclaimed' this tune for the piano – which I think brings a subliminal cohesion to a movement in which the pianist, so often in the background, can feel like the neglected guest at a party.

Even if Tchaikovsky had decided to complete the two further movements initially intended for his Third Concerto, this single-movement work would have remained a curiosity. It was written for Louis Diémer, the famous French pianist for whom Saint-Saëns would write his Fifth Concerto three years later (and, indeed, there are several moments which remind me of the French composer's Third Piano Concerto). The thematic material, although attractive and memorable, is perhaps too slight for the structure it

At one point in the cadenza of the Second Concerto's first movement, Tchaikovsky marks a passage with 12 *p*s (*pp* would mean 'very softly', *ppp* 'very, very softly' … and so on). A couple of pages later, in a sequence of blazing swagger, the marking is 12 *f*s (extremely loud) – dynamic indications totally off the charts, suggesting a composer driving the music, and the performer, to the edge of the precipice.

All these pieces exult in extremes and risk almost smothering the listener in their emotional enthusiasm. If Rachmaninov's concertos have the austere aura of a Russian icon hovering over them, perhaps Tchaikovsky's are more like the flame burning before the icon – one which, while intense, still envelops us in warm affection. Tchaikovsky is a composer from whom we either walk away in discomfort, or to whom we return constantly as a treasured friend. ●

Stephen Hough plays Tchaikovsky piano concertos at the Proms

Piano Concerto No. 1
Prom 31, 8 August

Piano Concerto No. 2
Prom 16, 28 July

Piano Concerto No. 3
Prom 1, 17 July

Concert Fantasia
Prom 57, 28 August

More Tchaikovsky at the Proms

Francesca da Rimini; Variations on a Rococo Theme
Prom 57, 28 August

Violin Concerto
Prom 34, 10 August

Manchester Art Gallery/Bridgeman Art Library (left); Lebrecht Music & Arts (right)

Chief Conductor Gianandrea Noseda

From 2011 the BBC Philharmonic will be based in a dedicated state-of-the-art studio at the BBC's new home in the North, mediacity, Salford Quays.

The BBC Philharmonic records programmes and concerts for Radio 3 and CDs for Chandos Records. It performs around 20 concerts a year at Manchester's magnificent Bridgewater Hall as well as giving concerts all around the North and touring internationally.

The Orchestra has built a worldwide reputation for outstanding quality and committed performances over a wide-ranging repertoire.

T: 0161 244 4001   E: philharmonic@bbc.co.uk

Jon Parker Lee

Visit us at bbc.co.uk/philharmonic

THSH

TOWN HALL BIRMINGHAM **SYMPHONY HALL** BIRMINGHAM

BOX OFFICE
0121 780 3333
www.thsh.co.uk

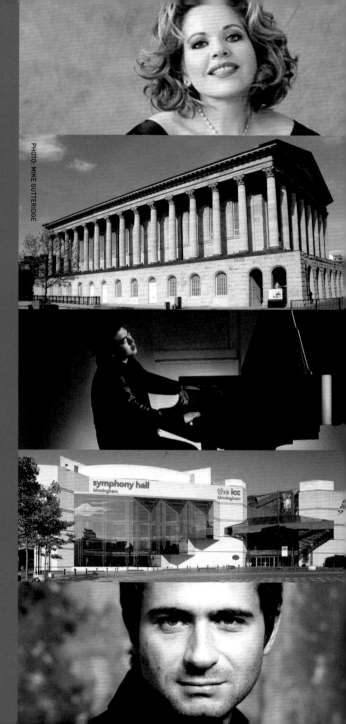

PHOTO: MIKE GUTTERIDGE

BIRMINGHAM INTERNATIONAL CONCERT SEASON 2009/10

SUBSCRIPTIONS ON SALE EARLY MAY

Highlights include:

Renée Fleming, Lang Lang,

Dallas Symphony Orchestra,

The Sixteen, Ian Bostridge,

Piotr Anderszewski and

Czech Philharmonic Orchestra

SUPPORTED BY
 Birmingham City Council

Registered charity No. 1053937

TH RENOVATION ALSO FUNDED BY

 Heritage LOTTERY FUNDED

Project Part-Financed by the European Union
European Regional Development Fund

BRIGHT YOUNG THINGS

As BBC Radio 3's New Generation Artists scheme celebrates a decade of championing young artists, Adam Gatehouse looks back over a rich crop of talent, and Clara Nissen talks to two distinguished alumni performing at this season's First and Last nights

One dark evening in February 1999 I was at home chopping vegetables when I turned on the radio. It was the slow movement of Beethoven's Violin Concerto. The playing of the violinist was sublime, totally out of the ordinary. I had to stop everything and just listen. Who was this? At the end the announcer told us it was the 19-year-old Georgian violinist Lisa Batiashvili, a name completely unknown to me, and to virtually everyone else at that time. There and then I resolved that she should be among the first to be invited to join Radio 3's New Generation Artists scheme, which was then in the early planning stages.

The original idea behind the scheme was simple and applies to this day: to invite a select group of outstanding young soloists and ensembles – not just from the UK but from all around the world – to perform and record for Radio 3 across a two-year period, and across a range of platforms. These include public concerts at major UK venues and festivals (including the Proms), studio recordings (for many, this is their first encounter with the studio microphone), appearances with the BBC orchestras and, in some cases, CDs co-produced with a record label.

Not all NGAs are selected while I conduct culinary experiments at home. I was told that a young group called the Jerusalem Quartet were worth listening to – I only had to hear two bars of the quartet playing Haydn in concert at the Wigmore Hall to know that here was a truly remarkable ensemble, with an average age at the time of 20, but who had already been playing together for seven years! Others do it the hard way: violist Lawrence Power bombarded us with letters, demanding to be heard. When I did, my jaw dropped.

All the NGAs are selected after a rigorous process of listening and attending concerts, and a wide consultation across the profession, from prominent musicians to producers. Our first list of artists now reads like a who's who of today's brilliant young musical talent, and all of them have gone on to build major international careers: alongside Batiashvili and the Jerusalem Quartet, they include pianists Paul Lewis, Steven Osborne and François-Frédéric Guy, cellists Natalie Clein and Alban Gerhardt, the Belcea Quartet and Leopold String Trio, flautist Emily Beynon, and singers Lisa Milne and Christopher Maltman.

Is there a typical New Generation Artist? The answer is that there are as many typical NGAs as there are NGAs themselves – each is a strong individualist who will approach music in his or her own way. Take pianist Simon Trpčeski – I first heard him in a performance of Prokofiev's Seventh Sonata of hair-raising brilliance. Later he brought his own special brand of poetic virtuosity to the Romantic repertoire – don't miss him on 31 August. Or mezzo-soprano Alice Coote – not only has she become one of the great Mahler singers of our time, but she is equally distinctive in Handel and Monteverdi. Catch her on the First Night.

But there are certain qualities shared by all 70 artists to have joined the scheme since it began. They need to be able to turn their hand to a variety of different styles and repertoire, from solo to chamber music and concerto work. They also need to have a hunger for repertoire and a substantial body of works under their belt before they come on to the scheme. We ask them to perform a lot of different music and, as everything they do for us is recorded for broadcast (often in Radio 3's *Lunchtime Concert* and *Afternoon on 3* strands), they can't simply repeat the same programme. And they need to be inquisitive and willing to collaborate freely – one of the joys of my job in running the New Generation Artists scheme is acting rather as a marriage-broker. We delight in bringing together many different artists in perpetually varying combinations. Some go on to form lasting partnerships.

Lately we have added two new elements to the scheme: jazz, with the appointment of pianist and composer Gwilym Simcock as our first jazz NGA in 2006 and, more recently, with trumpeter Tom Arthurs;

Cadogan Hall   Daniela Lehner   Tom Arthurs   Mahan Esfahani

New Generation Artists 10th-Anniversary Weekend
29–31 August, Cadogan Hall

This year the Proms marks the 10th anniversary of BBC Radio 3's New Generation Artists scheme with a three-day, 12-concert weekend at Cadogan Hall, featuring a small army of NGAs past and present – in addition to a sprinkling of NGA appearances in the evening Proms and the Monday-lunchtime Proms Chamber Music series.

Some of the most established NGAs are appearing – pianist **Simon Trpčeski**, flautist **Sharon Bezaly**, mezzo-soprano **Christine Rice** and baritone **Jonathan Lemalu**, among others – while exciting newcomers, jazz trumpeter **Tom Arthurs**, harpsichordist **Mahan Esfahani**, violinist **Tai Murray**, mezzo-soprano **Daniela Lehner**, cellist **Andreas Brantelid** and Finnish string quartet **Meta4**, make their Proms debuts.

Pianists **Ashley Wass** and Simon Crawford-Phillips complement this season's focus on Stravinsky ballets with *The Rite of Spring* in the composer's duet version, while celebrations of

the season's four major composer anniversaries include Mendelssohn's remarkable early Octet played by the **Jerusalem** and **Pavel Haas** quartets. Cellist **Natalie Clein**, violinist **Jennifer Pike**, tenor **Andrew Kennedy** and **Jonathan Lemalu** are among those performing works by Delius, Holst and Elgar in a concert marking 75 years since 1934, a landmark year in British music; and there are two specially commissioned new works: by jazz NGA **Tom Arthurs** and by John McCabe for pianist **Ashley Wass**.

With forces ranging from solo violin (**Alina Ibragimova** and **Tai Murray** in Bach and Bartók respectively) to eight cellos (in Villa-Lobos's arrangements of Bach Preludes and Fugues) and to four string quartets (in Van Bree's *Allegro*), the variety of artist groupings is as wide as the musical talent on offer.

For full details, see Listings, pages 134–136.

and early music, with the arrival of the wonderfully versatile Iranian harpsichordist Mahan Esfahani. These have opened up possibilities not only to extend the areas of repertoire we can feature but also to expand our range of collaborations.

You will be able to experience all of this and more at first hand throughout this season's Proms and particularly at this year's special NGA weekend (29–31 August, *see box above*) as part of an extended Proms Chamber Music series. Do join us to celebrate 10 years of these remarkable artists! ▶

Adam Gatehouse is Editor, Live Music and New Generation Artists, BBC Radio 3.

Elisabeth Blanchet (Lehner); Lou Mensah (Arthurs); K. T. Bruce (Esfahani)

Northern Sinfonia
Music Director, Thomas Zehetmair

"In less than four years The Sage Gateshead has become one of the world's most admired centres for music" *The Times, 7th October 2008*

www.thesagegateshead.org

Photography: Tony Griffiths, Dan Brady, North News & Pictures

north east england

Gateshead Council

ARTS COUNCIL ENGLAND

Alice Coote *mezzo-soprano*
(NGA, 2001–3) **Prom 1**

Adam Gatehouse invited me to become a New Generation Artist after he heard me replace Simon Keenlyside at short notice in a Radio 3 lunchtime recital. I think he could see a future for me as a recitalist, not just as an opera singer – until then I'd always been told you had to make your name in opera before you'd be offered recitals – so, when he asked me if I'd like to become an NGA, I jumped at the opportunity.

I didn't know how much work it was going to be, though! I suddenly realised why most singers don't work in all three areas of concerts, recitals and opera. I had to learn real discipline to add recital and concert repertoire to the opera roles I was already learning, something that has been useful to this day. Singing recitals is now the most meaningful part of my career, and probably the only opportunity a young singer gets to do recital work on any serious level is through the NGA scheme.

Adam also encouraged me to work with lots of different pianists and singers, and I went on to sing repertoire I probably wouldn't have done otherwise. It was through hearing my broadcasts on Radio 3 that Judith Weir says she fell in love with my voice. She wrote *The Voice of Desire* for me, which I then premiered at the Proms in 2003.

Alison Balsom *trumpet*
(NGA, 2004–6) **Prom 76**

I think Adam had considered solo trumpeters for the New Generation Artists scheme before I came along, but felt there wasn't a wide enough repertory. I took him a list of pieces that I wanted to play, which ran to six or seven pages. When he heard how passionate I was about the trumpet, particularly its quirky and contemporary British repertoire, I think he thought I should at least be given a chance.

I was given a surprisingly free rein. If I believed in a piece, I was given the opportunity to do it, whether it was played in a recording studio or on the concert stage, with or without a BBC orchestra. At one stage while on the scheme I found myself performing three big concertos and a recital in one week. I wasn't sure if I could physically do it but, if I was asked to do it again now, I'd say, 'Great! Bring it on!'

Early on in my career the media mainly focused on the fact I'm a blonde, female trumpeter. The BBC didn't select me for image reasons and that was a great vote of confidence.

New Generation Artists appearing at the Royal Albert Hall and in Monday-lunchtime Proms Chamber Music recitals at Cadogan Hall this season

Alison Balsom *trumpet* (2004–6)
Haydn Trumpet Concerto
Piazzolla Libertango
Gershwin, arr. Barry Forgie 'They can't take that away from me'
BBC commission: world premiere
Prom 76, 12 September

Belcea Quartet (1999–2001)
Haydn String Quartet in F sharp minor, Op. 50 No. 4
Britten String Quartet No. 2
PCM 3, 3 August

Alice Coote *mezzo-soprano* (2001–3)
Brahms Alto Rhapsody
Prom 1, 17 July

Colin Currie *percussion* (2003–5)
Bartók Sonata for two pianos and percussion
Prom 33, 9 August
Xenakis Aïs
Prom 63, 2 September

Alban Gerhardt *cello* (1999–2001)
Unsuk Chin Cello Concerto
BBC commission: world premiere
Prom 38, 13 August

Sally Matthews *soprano* (2002–4)
Mendelssohn Symphony No. 2, 'Lobgesang'
Prom 19, 30 July

Jennifer Pike *violin* (current NGA)
Holst A Song of the Night
Saint-Saëns Introduction and Rondo capriccioso
Prom 13, 26 July

Christine Rice *mezzo-soprano* (2004–6)
Sir Harrison Birtwistle The Mask of Orpheus – The Arches
Prom 39, 14 August

James Rutherford *bass-baritone* (2000–02)
Beethoven Symphony No. 9, 'Choral'
Prom 40, 15 August

Ailish Tynan *soprano* (2003–5)
Chabrier Ode à la musique
Prom 1, 17 July

Elizabeth Watts *soprano* (current NGA)
Haydn The Seven Last Words of Our Saviour on the Cross
Prom 6, 20 July

Llŷr Williams *piano* (2003–5)
Mendelssohn Prelude and Fugue in E minor, Op. 35 No. 1
J. S. Bach, transcr. Busoni Three Chorale Preludes
Brahms Variations and Fugue on a Theme by Handel, Op. 24
PCM 5, 17 August

Shai Wosner *piano* (current NGA)
Mozart Piano Concerto No. 20 in D minor, K466
Prom 55, 26 August

BBC SCOTTISH SYMPHONY
ORCHESTRA

ILAN VOLKOV, CHIEF CONDUCTOR
DONALD RUNNICLES, CHIEF CONDUCTOR DESIGNATE
STEFAN SOLYOM, ASSOCIATE GUEST CONDUCTOR

BBC PROMS SEASON INCLUDES
Ilan Volkov conducts Beethoven's 'Choral' Symphony and the world premiere of Unsuk Chin's Cello Concerto. Donald Runnicles conducts Strauss' Symphonia Domestica.

EDINBURGH INTERNATIONAL FESTIVAL 2009
Strauss' Don Quixote with Donald Runnicles, and David Robertson conducts Verdi's Macbeth.

CONCERT SEASON 2009/10
In his inaugural concerts as Chief Conductor Donald Runnicles conducts Mahler's First Symphony and Ravel's Daphnis and Chloe.

Ilan Volkov conducts the world premiere of a new work by Sir Peter Maxwell Davies. The orchestra will also present the complete cycle of Martinů's Piano Concertos and Rachmaninov's Symphonies.

"THIS HAS TO GO DOWN AS ONE OF THE MOST TERRIFYING, THRILLING EVENINGS AT THE PROMS THIS CENTURY… DONALD RUNNICLES LIFTED THE BBC SCOTTISH SYMPHONY ORCHESTRA TO A NEW PINNACLE." THE INDEPENDENT

bbc.co.uk/bbcsso

BBC Scotland

BBC RADIO 3 90–93FM

NEW MUSIC

From the very early days of the Proms, when Henry Wood began introducing his 'novelties', the Proms has led the way in championing new music, presenting first performances across the years of works by Schoenberg, Delius, Elgar and Bax, among others. Here, **Philip Clark** introduces this year's crop of 11 BBC commissions, and 15 further world, UK or London premieres

Philip Clark is a composer and writer specialising in new music, jazz and improvised music. He contributes to titles including *Gramophone*, *The Wire* and *International Piano*, and is currently writing a book on Dave Brubeck.

Louis Andriessen
(born 1939)

The Hague Hacking
UK premiere
Prom 43 17 **August**

Dutch composer Louis Andriessen is best known for music that explores his credo of hard-left politics, philosophy and spirituality – so it comes as a surprise that *The Hague Hacking*, for two pianos and orchestra, owes a debt to a *Tom and Jerry* cartoon. 'The opening refers to an existing piece, which was in my mind while composing,' explains the composer, 'but I couldn't track it down immediately.'

The piece turned out to be Liszt's *Hungarian Rhapsody* No. 2, which had entered Andriessen's memory through the 1946 *Tom and Jerry* episode *The Cat Concerto*, in which Tom is portrayed as a piano virtuoso who is accompanied by an off-screen orchestra. Andriessen says that at the end of his piece, 'as a kind of triumphant denouement', he subjects a popular Dutch song about The Hague to cartoon violence: cadence points hang mid-air and melodic hooks are chased down mouseholes.

Tom Arthurs
(born 1980)

And Distant Shore
BBC co-commission with the Royal Philharmonic Society: world premiere
PCM 18 30 August

Trumpeter, composer and improviser Tom Arthurs is only the second jazz artist to be taken up by BBC Radio 3's New Generation Artists scheme. He describes his music as 'one of assimilation rather than of fusion': alongside a huge range of jazz influences, he cites a fascination with the music of György Ligeti and even with the philosophies of the 'molecular gastronomy' pioneer, chef Ferran Adrià.

Arthurs's Proms commission will pair him with (classical) trumpeter Giuliano Sommerhalder in a piece drawing on the totality of his interests. 'I look for a seamless integration between improvisation and composition in my music,' he elucidates. 'Composition that sounds as free as if it were improvised, and improvisations so rich in form and content that you might think they were composed.'

Sir Richard Rodney Bennett
(born 1936)

Lilliburlero Variations
world premiere of orchestral version
Prom 13 26 July

The popular tune 'Lilliburlero' came into public consciousness as far back as 1689, when Henry Purcell included it in his anthology *Musick's Handmaid*. Its source is a matter of contention: Purcell may have 'borrowed' it for his book – but, if so, he recognised a melody of enduring quality.

'Lilliburlero' is one of those themes that everyone knows (even if they don't realise it), and in this set of variations Sir Richard Rodney Bennett counterpoints his own inventions with strategically reiterated melodic fragments from the original. The work opens with a full presentation of the melody, out of which he extrapolates Rachmaninov-like arpeggios, Debussyan harmonies and powerfully marching *moto perpetuos*. Originally written for two pianos, the piece will be heard at the Proms in a new version for full orchestra.

Cornelis de Bondt
(born 1953)

Doors Closed
London premiere
Prom 58 28 August

The music of Dutch composer Cornelis de Bondt (a former student of Louis Andriessen) is obsessed with ritual, and the subject of *Doors Closed* (1984), now widely regarded as a modern classic, is death.

Bondt instantaneously plunges the listener into a loaded sound-world as he superimposes the opening bars of the Funeral March from Beethoven's 'Eroica' Symphony onto Dido's Lament from Purcell's *Dido and Aeneas*. Initially, he disguises these *objets trouvés* but, as his ritualistic structure evolves, recognisable fragments float to the surface.

Putting together two iconic musical monuments from the past creates a third level of reality: Bondt's piece is a commentary on how composers have portrayed rituals surrounding death – his dramatic clash re-radicalises Purcell and Beethoven, making us hear them afresh.

Unsuk Chin
(born 1961)

Cello Concerto
BBC commission: world premiere
Prom 38 13 August

Born in Korea, Unsuk Chin has lived in Berlin since 1988, the year she completed her studies with György Ligeti. 'I try to render into music the visions of immense light and of an incredible magnificence of colours that I see in all my dreams,' she once explained. Initially she realised those dreamlike states through electronic means, but she has since made her name through a series of tautly conceived, timbrally kaleidoscopic orchestral, instrumental and operatic works.

Unlike her three previous concertos, this work, Chin says is about the 'competitiveness' between the soloist and orchestra. She sees the piece as sprouting from the 'aura' of the cello as the 'initial nucleus', and the soloist 'becomes a kind of illusionist, disguising the nature of the instrument', while accepting that 'the cello has a certain intrinsic emotional character which can't be denied'.

Sir Peter Maxwell Davies
(born 1934)

Violin Concerto No. 2
UK premiere
Prom 70 8 September

With a concerto each for trumpet, piano, horn, piccolo, violin and Northumbrian pipes, as well as the cycle of 10 Strathclyde Concertos (1986–96, for the principal players of the Scottish Chamber Orchestra), Sir Peter Maxwell Davies has engaged with a wide array of solo instruments.

At the time of writing his first violin concerto (1986) for the legendary American violinist Isaac Stern, he spoke about how Mendelssohn's Violin Concerto had influenced the work; so it's apt that one of the co-commissioners of his new concerto – modelled around the playing of Daniel Hope – should have been the Leipzig Gewandhaus Orchestra, which Mendelssohn himself led from 1835 until his death in 1847. For Maxwell Davies, writing concertos involves a 'disciplined kind of form … one could write something and call it a concerto but without that discipline it would be a cop-out.'

Ben Foskett
(born 1977)

new work
BBC commission:
world premiere
Prom 24 2 August

Paris-based British composer Ben Foskett makes his Proms debut this season and, at the time of going to press, is still working out which direction his new piece might take. 'When I start a work,' he explains, 'I tend towards bare pitches and rhythms as the source of inspiration. I'm prone to throw lots away when I write: sometimes, ridding myself of material that isn't working inspires me with the rest of the piece.'

In his Violin Concerto of 2004 for Clio Gould, premiered by the London Sinfonietta, Foskett reinterpreted the traditional soloist-versus-orchestra concerto model by making the soloist's music evolve independently of the orchestra's. He suggests something like that approach might colour this latest orchestral score: 'I try to use the orchestra as an ever-changing textural palette that is constantly expanding and contracting in different directions,' he says.

Gershwin (1898–1937), arr. Barry Forgie
(born 1939)

Shall We Dance –
'They can't take that away
from me'
BBC commission: world premiere
Prom 76 12 September

Sarah Connolly might be most renowned for her recent roles in Purcell's *Dido and Aeneas* and Gluck's *Orfeo ed Euridice*, but at one point she'd have happily swapped Covent Garden or La Scala, Milan, for the stage of Ronnie Scott's. She has described jazz singer Carmen McRae as 'one of the greatest interpreters of song ever' and, at one point, stopped singing classical repertoire altogether for a few months, to study the inscrutable art of scat-singing. For her Last Night appearance, alongside that of trumpeter Alison Balsom, BBC Big Band conductor and arranger Barry Forgie has made an arrangement for them both of Gershwin's classic 'They can't take that away from me'. This enduring standard, first sung by Fred Astaire, has been nurtured by the likes of Ella Fitzgerald, Frank Sinatra and Sarah Vaughan.

Detlev Glanert
(born 1960)

Shoreless River
BBC co-commission with
WDR Symphony Orchestra,
Cologne, Royal Concertgebouw
Orchestra, Amsterdam, and
National Symphony Orchestra,
Washington DC: UK premiere

Detlev Glanert is renowned for the unashamed Romanticism of his scores: Mahler, Schubert and Shostakovich are his idols.

As with his *Theatrum bestiarum*, commissioned for the 2005 Proms, Detlev Glanert's *Shoreless River* has its starting point in an opera project – in this case his forthcoming *Das Holzschiff* ('The Wooden Ship'). Here, the sea represents a shifting order, as the principal characters play out their erotically charged power games.

Although he has in the past derived orchestral works from operas, Glanert claims this is 'always a loose relationship. The instrumental works are a kind of musical "laboratory" where I can develop techniques and moods, without using the same music or subject.'

Philip Glass
(born 1937)

Symphony No. 7,
'A Toltec Symphony'
UK premiere
Prom 37 12 August

Despite the 'urban' sound-world of Philip Glass's music, a recurring theme has been the impact of man upon the environment. His Seventh Symphony explores the spiritual and environmental culture of the ancient Toltec people of Mesoamerica – a sophisticated civilisation that reached its peak between AD 700 and AD 1100.

'Like many indigenous traditions, the Toltecs emphasised the relationship with the forces of the natural world in developing their own wisdom,' Glass says, and his symphony is modelled around the similarly formed trinity of beliefs held by the present-day Huichol people of Mexico – revolving around The Corn, The Sacred Root and The Blue Deer. The three movements chart a course developing from Mother Earth, aspiring towards the attainment of absolute knowledge.

Goldie
(born 1965)

new work
BBC commission:
world premiere
Proms 21 & 23
1 & 2 August

Last year it was not to be. Comedian Sue Perkins pipped DJ and drum-and-bass pioneer Goldie to the post in BBC Two's *Maestro* competition, and claimed a conducting spot at London's Proms in the Park. But this year Goldie has got a Royal Albert Hall gig in the bag – as a composer. The producer and DJ, best known for his albums *Timeless* and *Sine tempus*, will create a new piece for the BBC Concert Orchestra based on the theme of evolution to celebrate the 150th anniversary of Charles Darwin's *On the Origin of Species*. The piece will be a watershed for him: Goldie usually builds albums and tracks with electronics and sound synthesis, but the BBC Two cameras will again trace his progress for a future documentary as he creates his first purely orchestral score.

Osvaldo Golijov
(born 1960)
after Schubert

She Was Here
UK premiere
Prom 59 29 August

She Was Here by the Argentinian composer Osvaldo Golijov is about his relationship with the music of Schubert. The piece occupies an intriguing hinterland between transcription, orchestration and recomposition, as Golijov 'borrows' four Schubert Lieder and uses an extended orchestral palette to find contemporary resonance within this iconic music.

The composer explains that his work was written 'at a time of loss and sadness'. But, he says, 'Schubert brings consolation … when he shows that past, present and future are only an illusion.' Through his new orchestral contexts, Golijov explores the distance between then and now, and he says that within these Schubert songs he hears anticipations of Berg, Glass, Stravinsky and Weill. By bringing these to the surface, Schubert is reclaimed as a perpetually contemporary presence.

Heinz Holliger
(born 1939)

(S)irató
UK premiere
Prom 26 4 August

Holliger explains that the Hungarian word 'Sirató' translates as 'lamenting song' and that in Italian 'irato' means 'furious': so '(S)irató' implies a lament tinged with anger.

The piece is dedicated to the Hungarian composer Sándor Veress (1907–92), Holliger's teacher, who spent most of his life in Switzerland. The particular combination of emotions in *(S)irató* stems from Holliger's perception that 'our country has much to thank Veress for', but that Veress received unfair treatment from officials while he was seeking Swiss nationality.

Holliger works with two distinct types of music: a slowly evolving orchestral monolith builds on the idea of a monody, while fractious instrumental soliloquies liberate themselves from the relentless onwards march. Holliger weaves in folk songs collected by Bartók and a part for the Hungarian cimbalom – Veress's homeland evoked by one of his closest Swiss friends.

Toshio Hosokawa
(born 1955)

Cloud and Light
UK premiere
Prom 10 24 July

In *Cloud and Light*, for shō and orchestra, by Hiroshima-born composer Toshio Hosokawa, East meets West but in the most subtle way imaginable. 'The shō is one of the oldest Chinese musical instruments,' Hosokawa explains. 'As an instrument used in *gagaku*, traditional Japanese court music, the shō acquired the musical character of Japan.'

Hosokawa was inspired by legendary shō player Mayumi Miyata. 'The sense of time from the instrument reminds me that time is spiralling and circling. The floating sounds, with faint changes of harmonies, appear as if light is radiating from the instrument.'

The title of the concerto derives from a painting showing 'Buddha on a cloud with musicians descending down to the land. I tried to depict the gradual descent of the cloud to the land from far away, growing with light, which is represented by the shō.'

Michael Jarrell
(born 1958)

Sillages
Orchestre de la Suisse Romande/ BBC commission: world premiere of expanded version

Prom 25 3 August

Geneva-born Michael Jarrell is Professor of Composition at the Hochschule für Musik in Vienna. His new triple concerto is about line, waves and shape. Jarrell explains that 'sillage' has multiple meanings for him: 'It's the trace that a ship leaves behind it on the surface of water,' he says, and he also sees it as a 'quill pen drawing a line on a blotter. The ink then takes on a life of its own as it impregnates the paper unevenly.'

The concerto begins with a striking, stripped-back gesture: the three soloists playing a unison A, the note musicians use for tuning up, which then 'smudges' to incorporate other pitches. 'The soundfield broadens,' Jarrell says, 'and these figures, born from the breath of the soloists, take on their own life in the symphonic ensemble surrounding them – the orchestra acts as a reflection, or distorting mirror.'

Oliver Knussen
(born 1952)

Cleveland Pictures
UK premiere
Prom 30 7 August

Oliver Knussen's relationship with the Proms dates back to 1976 with the UK premiere of *Océan de terre*. Three years later, in something of a coup for the then 27-year-old composer, Michael Tilson Thomas conducted the premiere of his Symphony No. 3, a work that later established itself as a contemporary classic. Since then Knussen has returned to the Proms many times, both as composer and conductor; most recently, in 2007, Leila Josefowicz wowed the Proms audience with his Violin Concerto.

At the time of writing, Knussen is still preparing *Cleveland Pictures*, to be premiered by The Cleveland Orchestra shortly before he conducts its UK premiere at the Proms with the BBC Symphony Orchestra, with which he takes up his new role as Artist-in-Association this summer. For Detlev Glanert, Knussen's music 'is totally without borders'. Knussen's gifts as a conductor are no less wide-ranging.

John McCabe
(born 1939)

Horn Concerto, 'Rainforest IV'
London premiere
Prom 67 5 September

Sonata (Study No. 12)
BBC commission: world premiere
PCM 16 30 August

McCabe's Horn Concerto was premiered in Cardiff in 2007 by the BBC National Orchestra of Wales and soloist David Pyatt, who join forces for its London premiere at the Proms. The composer describes it as contrasting the urban chic of the French horn as used in 1950s and 1960s jazz and the evocation of a spacious, mist-filled rainforest.

His latest piano work is part of a series of Studies dedicated to composers he admires. 'What I love about Tippett's piano music, and why this piece is dedicated to him,' he explains, 'is his ability to conjure up wonderful textures and exploit the piano's resources fully. His writing is not really idiomatic, but it doesn't matter – the essence of the music is so powerful.'

Anna Meredith
(born 1978)

new work
BBC commission: world premiere
Prom 32 9 August

In *froms*, her commission for the 2008 Last Night of the Proms, young Scottish composer Anna Meredith took advantage of the geographical spread of the BBC orchestras at Proms in the Park events to produce a work simultaneously performed in Glasgow, Swansea, Belfast and London. The exuberant whole was drawn together by satellite link-ups.

The forces for her new piece, for two pianos and chamber orchestra, may be more modest, but her enthusiasm is clear. Meredith recently completed an opera for teenagers, *Tarantula in Petrol Blue*, for performance in Aldeburgh, but her mind has turned to her latest Proms piece. 'I'm looking forward to writing a piece with the energy of the two pianists,' she says, 'pitting them against each other, or perhaps teaming them up like a monster-piano versus the orchestra.'

Michael Nyman
(born 1944)

The Musicologist Scores
BBC commission: world premiere
Prom 54 25 August

When the Michael Nyman Band follows the Orchestra of the Age of Enlightenment onto the stage on 25 August, they'll be putting a modern spin on music by anniversary composers Purcell and Handel. Sections from Nyman's score to Peter Greenaway's 1982 film *The Draughtsman's Contract* were derived from Purcell originals, and *Memorial* – heard in the soundtrack to *The Cook, The Thief, His Wife and Her Lover* – was founded on material from Purcell's semi-opera *King Arthur*. Nyman's new Proms commission will revisit music by Handel using his own distinctive Minimalist signature.

For Nyman, who studied with Baroque music specialist Thurston Dart, the two styles are freely connected: 'My use of closed variation forms with repetitive harmonic systems has as much to do with the Baroque as with Minimalism,' he says.

Rebecca Saunders
(born 1967)

traces
UK premiere of revised version
Prom 56 27 August

London-born composer Rebecca Saunders has lived in Germany for most of her adult life, and brings to the Proms a 'thoroughly revised and expanded' version of this work, which had its premiere in Hamburg during 2006. A former student of the German composer Wolfgang Rihm and of British composer Nigel Osborne, her sound-world and aesthetic concerns have been indelibly formed by Central European experiences.

Her own programme note on the piece quotes from Italo Calvino and Samuel Beckett. How do these thoughts filter into her music? 'They provide a parallel to the music itself,' she says. 'The Beckett quotation underlines that the music refers to itself and is a complete and autonomous object which should require no explanation. *traces* is a sonic exploration of a reduced and, for me, special palette of sounds and colours, which I have distilled into a single form.'

Alfred Schnittke
(1934–98)

Nagasaki
UK premiere
Prom 52 24 August

Nagasaki is early Schnittke, written in 1958 when he was still a student at the Moscow Conservatory; but, out of frank borrowings from Carl Orff and Shostakovich, a mature style feels ready to emerge.

The work is a reimagining of a Baroque oratorio that expresses horror over the atomic bomb released over Nagasaki in 1945. Schnittke later commented, 'It might be a fairly naive piece by modern standards, but it is a work where I was absolutely sincere.' Perhaps the naivety applies to the third movement, 'On That Fateful Day', where white-noise sonorities, shrieking glissandos and shouts from the chorus portray the bomb's explosive impact.

Schnittke's instinct told him his finale should be tragic in tone, while the all-powerful Soviet Composers' Union demanded an upbeat close. Schnittke's surface optimism went some way to mollifying the Party – and he began a lifetime of writing works with subliminal subtexts.

Peter Thompson (McCabe), Libi Pedder (Nyman), Katrin Schander (Saunders), Sikorski Edition (Schnittke)

Augusta Read Thomas
(born 1964)

Violin Concerto No. 3, 'Juggler in Paradise'
BBC co-commission with Radio France, Mr & Mrs Bill Brown and National Symphony Orchestra, Washington DC: UK premiere
Prom 72 8 September

American composer Augusta Read Thomas explains that 'Juggler in Paradise', the subtitle for her new violin concerto, is 'intended to suggest, or invoke, the image of the violin's role – playing a kind of rhapsodic cadenza throughout – as a counterpoint to paradisiacal constellations in the orchestra'.

The soloist and orchestra take very defined roles. The composer explains: 'harp, celesta, piano and percussion together form a kind of "helix" of bell sounds ... always kaleidoscopic in colour and sometimes with string pizzicatos.' The violinist interweaves around this flow of sound. 'A metaphor might be,' Read Thomas says, 'the works of the painter Seurat: there are "dots" of "bells" everywhere – no two ever the same.'

Claude Vivier
(1948–83)

Orion
UK premiere
Prom 60 30 August

Montreal-born composer Claude Vivier met the saddest of ends, as he was murdered in his Paris apartment in 1983, at the age of 34. Vivier was a curiously otherworldly, visionary man, a onetime Stockhausen student who listened hard to the indigenous music of Bali and Japan, and had his ears opened to a new melodic sensibility and the potential of tuning systems that stretched beyond conventional Western thought.

Orion, written in 1979, suggests that human nature mirrors the unfathomable dimensions of the cosmos. Written for an appropriately vast orchestra with a cosmic-sized percussion section, the work blossoms from a noble trumpet melody that Vivier floats into new orbits, continually deconstructing it and reordering fragments into fresh constellations. To look inwards, Vivier reached to the furthest corners of the universe.

Jörg Widmann
(born 1973)

Con brio
UK premiere
Prom 18 29 July

Munich-born Jörg Widmann is a clarinettist and composer whose works probe the tenets of the Western tradition. His String Quartet No. 5 is an example of his oblique look at music of the past, entitled *Attempt at the Fugue*.

The reference point for *Con brio* is Beethoven. Mariss Jansons asked him for a piece to be programmed alongside Beethoven's Seventh and Eighth Symphonies. 'I don't quote a single note from Beethoven,' Widmann explains, 'it's the expression I take over.' 'Con brio' translates literally as 'with spirit', and Widmann aims to reflect the Beethovenian spirit by deploying a Classical-sized complement of brass and exploring how Beethoven's exuberant orchestral sound, his rhythmic mannerisms and searching harmonic ear might be uncorked for a new age. The piece, he says, portrays 'a festive-celebrating overture, larded with furious scherzo elements'.

John Woolrich
(born 1954)

Capriccio
world premiere
PCM 4 10 August

London-based John Woolrich, now in his mid-50s, describes *Capriccio* as a 'concertante for violin and strings'. The idea of concertantes – ensemble music with prominent solo parts – has been a recurring theme in his music, with precedents including *Ulysses Awakes* (1989, for viola and 10 solo strings) and *Another Staircase Overture* (1994), a latter-day concerto grosso.

Woolrich suggests the new piece will be 'quick, capricious and dark', and that the imagery of the *Caprichos* by the Spanish artist Francisco Goya has haunted the composition process. Woolrich has worked with the Scottish Ensemble and violinist Jonathan Morton before, and he believes in building enduring relationships with performers. His music in general, he claims, 'is not hard-edged. There are acerbities and abrasions – flatulent trombones, sawn-off oxygen cylinders ... but the attitude is benevolent.'

Ryan Wigglesworth
(born 1979)

new work
BBC commission: world premiere
Prom 8 22 July

Ryan Wigglesworth, 30 this year, combines a career as a conductor and composer – he has conducted operas by Strauss and Mozart, and worked with elite groups such as the Ensemble Modern and Ensemble Intercontemporain.

As a composer Wigglesworth has a particular affection for the BBC Symphony Orchestra (which has programmed a new song-cycle for its 2009/10 season). His new Proms piece celebrates the 800th anniversary of Cambridge University, where he lectures in music. 'To write consecutive works for the same orchestra is a precious gift,' he remarks. 'After the BBC SO premiered *Sternenfall* [in 2008] I began to conceive of ideas for a second work, and the challenge of producing music that takes advantage of the Royal Albert Hall's combination of vastness and intimacy is its own creative stimulus.'

Dan Rent (Thomas), J. A. Billard (Vivier), Maurice Foxall (Woolrich), Sophie Siem (Wigglesworth)

GLYNDEBOURNE
ON TOUR 2009

MOZART
COSÌ FAN TUTTE
A revival of Nicholas Hytner's celebrated 2006 Festival production

VERDI
FALSTAFF
A new production from the 2009 Festival, directed by Richard Jones

JANÁČEK
JENŮFA
A revival of the 2004 Festival production, part of Nikolaus Lehnhoff's iconic Janáček trilogy for Glyndebourne

GLYNDEBOURNE	13-31 OCTOBER
WOKING	3-7 NOVEMBER
STOKE-ON-TRENT	10-14 NOVEMBER
NORWICH	17-21 NOVEMBER
MILTON KEYNES	24-28 NOVEMBER
PLYMOUTH	1-5 DECEMBER

Join the Tour mailing list FREE to receive advance information.
Register at **www.glyndebourne.com**
or **telephone 01273 815000**

'The best opera I have experienced in England has been in the 'regions'... Glyndebourne mounts productions that are musically and dramatically flawless.'
GERMAINE GREER, *THE GUARDIAN*

GLYNDEBOURNE ON TOUR 09

kings place

SUMMER SEASON 2009
14 April – 28 June

FOLKWORKS: FIDDLES ON FIRE
BEETHOVEN UNWRAPPED
FINDING FAURÉ: Schubert Ensemble
LOUVRE MUSICAL PICTURES
ORCHESTRA of the AGE of ENLIGHTENMENT
EAST MEETS WEST
SOUND CENSUS: Endymion
PARIS JAZZ

ROYAL ACADEMY of MUSIC

Including 45 minute concerts
kp45' tickets from £6.50 online

AUTUMN SEASON 7 September – 20 December On Sale 12 June

www.kingsplace.co.uk   Box office: 020 7520 1490

photo © Keith Paisley

A FRENZY OF FINGERWORK

This year the Proms celebrates the wide variety of works for multiple pianos, from intimate Mozart to striking Stravinsky to new works. Harriet Smith offers a key to the season's pickings

While the piano duet might evoke images of cosy parlours, politely behaved children in Sunday best and amateur music-making at its most genteel, put two (or more) pianos together and you get something altogether different. A party, in fact – though one that can get rather out of hand, especially when you invite along other guests, such as percussion (as in the case of Bartók and Stravinsky); invoke the devilry of Paganini (as in Lutosławski) or hardcore techno house music (as in Louis Andriessen); or present it as the epitome of mechanistic mayhem (as in the case of George Antheil and John Adams).

Of course that initial imagery is hardly the whole picture – just think of the profoundly beautiful piano duet offerings of Mozart, Schubert and Fauré. The latter's suite, *Dolly*, is surely one of the most instantly recognisable duets ever written, but it is far more than just the epitome of Gallic charm: it's a nostalgic paean not only to childhood, but to the fading 19th century as well. Henri Rabaud's sensitive translation to orchestra of 1906 – which opens the first of two concerts on Multiple Pianos day (9 August) – captures its spirit perfectly.

Mozart's Double Concerto, springing out of the Baroque multi-keyboard concerto but with an entirely modern

Bartók performing alongside his second wife, Ditta Pásztory

virtuosity, was probably intended to be played by him and his sister. And it's striking how familial relationships are a recurrent theme in multi-piano repertoire, most famously, the Labèque sisters. They'll be playing, among other works, Poulenc's Double Concerto. How wonderful to have been in Venice in September 1932, when Poulenc premiered this delightful work at the Biennale, partnered by Jacques Février. He wrote it for the Princesse de Polignac (born Winnaretta Singer). She'd acquired her title by marriage but brought to the deal a tidy sum, courtesy of her father, king of the sewing-machine boom. She proceeded to lavish her fortune on composers and artists, and she must surely have been thrilled with this offering, with its irrepressible mix of black-and-white movie melodrama, humour and heart-stopping fragility, crowned by a melting Mozartian slow movement, experienced, as it were, through the fug of Gauloises.

George Antheil and John Adams got rather rockier receptions when they presented to the world *Ballet mécanique* (1926) and *Grand Pianola Music* (1982) respectively. In the case of Antheil, it led to wholesale rethinking. The piece had been intended as a soundtrack to a film by the painter Fernand Léger and cinematographer Dudley Murphy. Unfortunately communication was minimal, and the music ended up twice as long as the film. But it was also a logistical nightmare: the original version called for 16 player pianos, percussion, aeroplane propellers and two 'normal' pianos. Antheil reworked it several times, and by the time of his 1953 revision it was a model of comparative restraint, using only four pianos, plus percussion and propellers. Adams was so taken aback by the booing that greeted his *Grand Pianola Music* (for two pianos, wind, brass and three female voices) that he offered to 'take it down behind the barn and shoot it'. Much of the initial hostility sprang from the quality of

the performance itself, and the work – which Adams has described as 'Beethoven and Rachmaninov soaking in the same warm bath as Liberace, Wagner, The Supremes, Charles Ives and John Philip Sousa' – has since established itself as a firm favourite. There is a delicacy to much of it that is striking.

For other composers, though, it is the percussive qualities of the piano, and the possibilities of a huge dynamic range, that are paramount. Stravinsky followed *The Rite of Spring* with a new ballet that took the ritual but pared down the colour. In fact, *Les noces* is virtually monochrome, its pulsing rhythms and restricted forces of singers, chorus, percussion and four pianos creating a hypnotic effect. Bartók, in his Sonata for two pianos and

> Adams was so taken aback by the booing that greeted his *Grand Pianola Music* that he offered to 'take it down behind the barn and shoot it'.

percussion (premiered by him and his second wife in 1938), exploits the natural timbres of his forces not only to percussive but also to unexpectedly sensual effect. All four of these works – by Antheil, Adams, Stravinsky and Bartók – can be heard in the evening Prom of Multiple Pianos day.

But often it is the virtuoso possibility of two pianos that entices composers to this medium. Lutosławski made that apparent by choosing 'that' theme by the most famous virtuoso of all time, Paganini. Saint-Saëns, meanwhile, was so concerned that the frivolity of *The Carnival of the Animals* might damage his reputation that only one movement, 'The Swan', was published in his lifetime. And if the elegant bird, represented by the cello, was the epitome of Romantic serenity, it is the two pianists who provide the mischief, especially when let loose in their very own movement, parodying bad practice with out-of-kilter scales. It's all a far cry from those genteel duets. ●

Following periods as Editor of BBC Music Magazine and International Record Review, Harriet Smith combines her passion for music and gardening as a freelance journalist, editor and broadcaster.

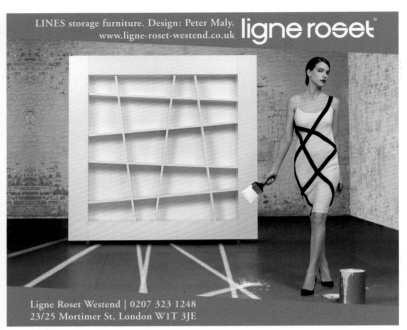

INDIAN VOICES

Viram Jasani introduces a day-long Proms celebration of India's myriad vocal styles – ranging from traditional *khyal* singing to a shoulder-shaking Bollywood climax – with a chance to get your dancing shoes on in Kensington Gardens

India is the home of one of the oldest and richest of the world's musical traditions, and vocal music has always been at its heart: in fact instruments evolved there only to emulate the fluidity and virtuosity of the voice. Following on from recent all-day events at the Proms celebrating the worlds of brass instruments and folk music, on 16 August the Proms presents a colourful spectrum of music focusing on the voice, featuring some of the most exciting names in Indian music.

It is the single vocal melodic line that characterises the 'solo' nature of Indian music – creating a platform for self-expression and evoking a sense of the spiritual. Even in duets, a single melodic line prevails, with artists either singing the same melody together or improvising in turn. The melodic line is accompanied by rhythmic percussion instruments such as tabla, and also by the tanpura (drone lute), which underpins the music with a hypnotic, sustained pitch. These three elements – single melodic line, rhythm, drone – are fundamental to all Indian music – even to the Bollywood music of the film industry (though this has now begun to show the Western influence of harmony and

Indian Voices culminates in a Bollywood extravaganza

counterpoint). From ancient Vedic recitation through the huge variety of folk music to the incredible virtuosity of modern classical singing, the fundamental instrument of Indian music has always been the voice.

The Proms Indian Voices day begins with a morning concert, showcasing the best of north Indian classical music in the vocal style known as *khyal*, with its associations of courtly patronage and the music rooms of palaces and *havelis* (private mansions). Pandit **Ram Narayan** (*opposite centre*) is perhaps the greatest player of the sarangi (short-necked fiddle) today. Praised by Yehudi Menuhin and Mstislav Rostropovich, he was a key figure in elevating this beautiful instrument from the status of accompanying vocalists to giving great solo performances. The sarangi has always had very close links with vocal traditions in India and comes nearest to emulating the voice. Pandits **Rajan and Sajan Mishra** are brothers from a great sarangi-playing family; they are considered among the foremost singers in India today, representing the Varanasi tradition of Uttar Pradesh. Their tremendous intonation and vocal timbre – along with great virtuosity and imagination – combine to produce magical performances. **Manjiri Asnare Kelkar** (*opposite left*) is a rising star and a brilliant beacon for the younger generation. She represents another old tradition of vocal *khyal* – the Jaipur–Gwalior tradition. Australian-born Devissaro created and leads **Asima** – a brilliant vocal ensemble from Kerala in south India. His use of harmony and counterpoint within the ensemble is in direct contrast to India's solo traditions, and yet the music retains a distinctly Indian sound. The group's repertoire ranges from Vedic chant to contemporary pop.

The afternoon event in Kensington Gardens features folk music from **Gujarat** and the desert of **Rajasthan**. The vocal traditions here are rich and vibrant, and the sheer power of the singers is startling. The songs cover a wide range of subjects, including welcomes, marriages, love, separation, devotion; and in the case of Gujarat they accompany the famous 'circle dances' *ras* and *garba*. Young people are the lifeblood of these groups – evidence that the tradition of Indian music is still thriving.

Indian Voices reaches its climax in the evening with a boisterous Bollywood Prom. India's film industry is now celebrated around the world, and its music and dance have inevitably changed over the decades. Borrowing from Western music, Indian classically trained singers and great poets, Bollywood music has achieved a much wider appeal because the films are seen as entertainment rather than art movies.

Shaan (Shantanu Mukherjee, *opposite right*) is one of the most versatile and talented younger-generation singers, having performed some of the most famous songs as a 'playback' singer for successful Bollywood films. He has become a household name as host of the TV talent shows *Sa Re Ga Ma Pa* (Zee TV) and *Star Voice of India* (Star Plus), and won all the top accolades at the Bollywood Movie Awards in 2007 for 'Chand sifarish' from the film *Fanaa* and in 2008 for 'Jab se tere naina' from *Saawariya*. A hit with audiences of all ages, he performs at the Proms alongside his band and dancers from Honey's Dance Academy.

Traditional Indian music is sometimes regarded as facing gradual extinction, becoming lost to the fast-moving modern electronic music aimed at a global market. On 16 August the Proms presents proof not only that India's ancient musical traditions are thriving today, but also that the country has produced a vibrant and equally authentic culture of contemporary vocal music and dance. ●

Sitarist Viram Jasani is CEO of the Asian Music Circuit, and curator of Indian Voices at the Proms.

Indian Voices day at the Proms

HALL

Including concerts by ...

Dmitri Hvorostovsky | **David Daniels** | Joshua Bell | **Leif Ove Andsnes**
Steven Isserlis | **Thomas Adès** | Frederica von Stade | **Matthias Goerne**
András Schiff | **Angelika Kirchschlager** | Mark Padmore | **Hagen Quartet**
Ton Koopman | **Christine Brewer** | Piotr Anderszewski | **Joyce DiDonato**
The English Concert | **Paul Lewis** | Simon Keenlyside | **Sara Mingardo**
Anna Caterina Antonacci | **Alice Coote** | Quatuor Ebène | **Florestan Trio**
Julia Fischer | **Christian Zacharias** | Thomas Quasthoff | **Ian Bostridge**
Akademie für Alte Musik Berlin | **Nash Ensemble** | Jerusalem Quartet
Belcea Quartet | Till Fellner | **Academy of Ancient Music** | Truls Mørk
Brad Mehldau | Michael Collins
... and many more of the world's leading musicians

TICKETS FOR SEPTEMBER – DECEMBER 2009 ON SALE NOW

Visit www.wigmore-hall.org.uk for full details and to book, or call the Box Office on 020 7935 2141.
For a free brochure email brochure@wigmore-hall.org.uk with your full postal address
(quoting 'BBC Proms') or call the Box Office.

To receive advance notice of all Wigmore Hall events, priority booking for Wigmore Series concerts,
10% off all Wigmore Hall Live CDs and many other benefits, become a Friend of Wigmore Hall.
Visit www.wigmore-hall.org.uk/friends, email friends@wigmore-hall.org.uk or phone 020 7258 8230 for full details.

Wigmore Hall, 36 Wigmore Street, London W1U 2BP. Director John Gilhooly
The Wigmore Hall Trust. Registered Charity No. 1024838 www.wigmore-hall.org.uk Box Office: 020 7935 2141

PROMS LEARNING

Education and family events at the Proms have gathered an unstoppable momentum in recent years, as **Andrew Stewart** discovers. With a whole host of free activities designed for people of all ages and abilities, there really is something for everyone. The only hard part is deciding which of the many events to attend …

A young violinist picks up tips in a Proms Family Orchestra worskhop

I t would be hard, perhaps impossible, to imagine a time when listeners had a greater choice or easier access to music than they have today. Just looking at the variety, global reach and inclusivity of this year's Proms shows how things have changed for audiences, how old barriers have been removed and new access points have been built in their place. Proms Learning has played a vital part in making sense of the many musical choices for Proms newcomers. Over the past decade it has helped thousands to discover the Proms for the first time, connecting new audience members with the life-enhancing power of classical music and enriching their listening experiences.

There's another side to the Proms Learning programme, one that has grown over the past five or six years and introduced many thousands more to the practical thrill of making music. Participation in performance is the deal, and no small deal either, given the opportunities for everyone from absolute beginners to skilled amateurs to play or sing in company with professional musicians from the BBC's performing groups. 'It's about opening up the Proms to as many people as possible,' observes Proms Learning Manager, Ellara Wakely. She adds that families really are welcome as part of the participatory mix. 'We feel that, if you participate, you're so much more likely to gain something extra from what music has to offer. That experience is available to families, individuals, young or old, anyone who wants to explore making music.'

Thanks to the BBC's *I Was There* webpage, Proms Learning participants have the chance to watch and listen to their own performances online. 'Making music and listening are all part of the Proms experience,' says Wakely. 'Playing with a Proms Family Orchestra might be your first taste of the Proms and lead you into exploring concerts at the Royal Albert Hall.' Such a likely result would show why the words Proms and learning fit so well together.

PROMS FAMILY ORCHESTRA

As the Proms Family Orchestra goes from strength to strength with its Proms debut performance this year, there are plenty of opportunities for new recruits to get involved throughout the season. The Proms Family Orchestra gives all family members the chance to take part, whether they are keen amateurs or have never played in an orchestra before. Charles Darwin's bicentenary, meanwhile, offers the best possible reason to convene a Darwin Family Orchestra, culminating in short post-workshop performances at the Natural History Museum on 1 and 2 August. The Proms Indian Voices day (16 August) offers more opportunity to participate, whether in a Bollywood dance session, the Bollywood Family Orchestra and Chorus with special guests Bollywood Brass, or to hear some of the best folk musicians India has to offer, all free as part of Indian Voices in the Park in Kensington Gardens.

Since its creation in 2006, the Proms Family Orchestra has placed mums, dads, children and extended family members alongside professional musicians from the BBC performing groups. The Family Orchestra sessions, open to all ages and musical abilities, have crafted pieces in response to everything from last year's Doctor Who Prom to the music of Karlheinz Stockhausen. Before the Proms Family Orchestras, the idea of performing in a Royal Albert Hall Prom was perhaps the stuff of dreams.

Sheila Hill and her son are veteran BBC Family Orchestra members. Sheila recalls Errollyn Wallen's Proms Family Orchestra commission from last year and the feelings attached to creating a new work. 'It was an amazing experience, simply amazing,' she says. 'I've certainly never seen anything like this, where adults and children are able to work so closely together. It's incredible that professional musicians take part and that everyone is treated with equal respect. There's an atmosphere of ▶

Chris Christodoulou (p.72, Proms Family Orchestra, Royal Albert Hall, 2008; & p.73)

Proms events for all the family

Family Music Intro
Royal College of Music
Saturday 25 July, 5.45pm–6.30pm
Monday 27 July, 5.15pm–6.00pm
Saturday 8 August, 5.15pm–6.00pm
Sunday 9 August, 1.15pm–2.00pm
Monday 10 August, 5.45pm–6.30pm
Sunday 30 August, 5.45pm–6.30pm
Monday 31 August, 5.45pm–6.30pm
Free (see Listings for details)

Proms Family Orchestra
Royal College of Music
(except * Kensington Gardens)
Saturday 1 August, 2.00pm–4.00pm
Sunday 2 August, 2.00pm–4.00pm
Saturday 8 August, 2.00pm–4.00pm
Sunday 16 August, 2.00pm–4.00pm*
Monday 31 August, 2.00pm–4.00pm
Free. To book places, please visit bbc.co.uk/proms, email promslearning @bbc.co.uk or call 020 7765 0643

Family Proms
Royal Albert Hall
Sunday 26 July, 11.00am–1.00pm
Saturday 1 August, 11.00am–1.00pm
Sunday 2 August, 11.00am–1.00pm
(See Listings for details)

Budapest Festival Orchestra Family Concert
Royal College of Music
Wednesday 18 August, 5.15pm–6.15pm
Free (see page 127 for details)

Indian Voices in the Park
Kensington Gardens
Sunday 16 August, 2.00pm–6.00pm
Free (see page 69 for details)

Proms Singing Day
Royal Albert Hall
Sunday 6 September, 2.00pm–4.00pm
Come and join in our Proms Family Chorus. *Free (see page 79 for details)*

people working together on something they love.' Making music with professional players has clearly inspired Sheila's son too. 'I've learnt how to interact with other musicians and play exactly on time,' he explains. 'There's nothing like this at my school!'

Suzan Beyazit, a guitarist and composer, and her 7-year-old daughter, Ezo, love the Family Orchestra's energy and versatility. 'I've learnt so much by playing in the percussion section,' Suzan observes, adding that the Family Orchestra's flexible nature encourages members to discover new skills. 'The important thing is that we are making music without pressure. It's not scary and we're all enjoying ourselves.'

Appearing at the Proms, says Suzan, will be both a challenge and an enriching experience for Family Orchestra and Chorus members. 'We really can be part of history.'

PROMS FAMILY ORCHESTRA GOES NORTH

Last year saw the hugely successful Proms Folk Day bring you live music, dance, storytelling and all things folk wrapped up in a day-long festival of activities. In 2009 Proms Learning has sought participation from families of all musical abilities to build a new Proms Family Orchestra in Salford and London. Combining members of earlier Proms Family Orchestras in London and bringing them together with new members from Salford, the Family Orchestra will work with musicians from the BBC Philharmonic on a newly devised piece inspired by Britten's *Young Person's Guide to the Orchestra* to be performed on 26 July as part of this year's free Family Prom.

> 'I went home feeling confident about composing for instruments that I hardly knew anything about before.'

Alexandra Wright (Inspire Day)

Shutterstock/Premm Design

INSPIRE – YOUNG COMPOSERS, STEP FORWARD

BBC Proms Inspire, now in its 11th year, offers young composers aged between 12 and 18 the opportunity to explore new musical frontiers, share ideas, work with professional players and composers, and meet other young composers. 'Inspire aims to give the broadest range of young talent across the UK the opportunity to explore their musical boundaries, new ways of composing, and get a taste of what it means to be a composer in the 21st century,' observes Proms Learning Manager, Ellara Wakely.

A series of national Composer Labs, begun in February, have already set this year's Inspire programme running, providing opportunities for young talents to work with leading composers, members of the BBC performing groups and BBC Proms Learning team – in workshop sessions in London, Manchester, Glasgow and Cardiff. Here, ideas ▶

Inspire

Do you know someone who should be entering the BBC Proms Inspire Young Composers' Competition, for 12- to 18-year-olds?

The deadline for entries is Friday 29 May 2009.

The 2009 Inspire Day, including the Young Composers' Concert at the Royal College of Music, will be held on Friday 14 August.
For more details, visit bbc.co.uk/proms, email promslearning@bbc.co.uk or call 020 7765 0643

were exchanged and tested, new friendships formed and skills developed. And fresh confidence took root among composers working in a wide variety of styles.

The BBC Proms Inspire Young Composers' Competition offers young composers a further opportunity. Each of this year's competition winners, chosen by a panel of top composers, will have their original works performed by the Aurora Orchestra in a Young Composers' Concert at the Royal College of Music as part of the BBC Proms Inspire Day on 14 August. They will also receive a commission from the BBC, to be performed by professional musicians at future Inspire events.

This year's competition is open for entries until 29 May, so if you're aged between 12 and 18, get composing! All entrants are invited to attend the Inspire Day – a great opportunity to meet professional composers, chat with performers and discover what their musical peers are up to – and of course, to experience a Prom at the Royal Albert Hall.

OUT+ABOUT

Proms Out+About has been taking the Proms to an eclectic range of venues for many years, bringing free live classical music to new audiences and making music with communities across London and the South-East.

Last year's Out+About programme included a 10-hour nomadic concert given by BBC Symphony Orchestra musicians around London, beginning with a morning appearance at the Marks & Spencer Pantheon store on Oxford Street and including slots at University College

Hospital, Heathrow Terminal 5, St Pancras International station and the British Museum. Watch out for an even wider spread of Out+About events across London this year on Thursday 25 June, when free live performances from the BBC Symphony Orchestra will draw families to some even more unusual locations. To find out more, visit bbc.co.uk/proms. ▶

Simon Jay Price (below left & right, Proms Out+About, British Museum, 2008)

'The orchestra was fantastic, the music outstanding, the choir tremendous and the whole event absolutely brilliant! The musicianship of the people involved with leading the session was brilliant. We both thoroughly enjoyed ourselves and would love to do it again.'

Jane Pullen (Doctor Who Prom and Proms Family Orchestra)

NationalTheatre

War Horse
New London Theatre

based on a novel by
Michael Morpurgo
adapted by Nick Stafford
in association with
Handspring Puppet Company

**Now Playing
in the West End**

Travelex **£10** Tickets
NationalTheatre

Death and the King's Horseman

by Wole Soyinka
Now Playing

Time and the Conways

by J B Priestley
Now Playing

The Observer

a new play by
Matt Charman
From 13 May

All's Well That Ends Well

Travelex **£10** Tickets
NationalTheatre

by William Shakespeare
From 19 May

Phèdre

by Jean Racine
in a version by Ted Hughes
From 4 June

World-class theatre, bars and restaurants with river views, specialist bookshop, free music and exhibitions.

nationaltheatre.org.uk

ARTS COUNCIL ENGLAND

War Horse
The Observer

Sponsored by

accenture
High performance. Delivered.

Death and the King's Horseman
All's Well that Ends Well

TRAVELEX £10 TICKETS   Media Partner
Sponsored by

Travelex worldwide money   THE TIMES   **sky**ARTS   Television
Media Partner

Phèdre

Sponsored by

Coutts

FAMILY MUSIC INTRO

Families are always welcome at the BBC Proms, with half-price tickets for under-16s available for all concerts (except the Last Night).

Family Music Intro offers a family-friendly series within the Proms Plus events at the Royal College of Music. Taking place before seven specially selected Proms across the season, each introduction promises to reveal fascinating facts about the music to be heard in the following concert, providing anyone over the age of 7 with illuminating insights into the world of performance, and generally bringing families into contact with how music is brought to life. There's a focus on dance, for example, in the Family Music Intro event on 27 July; while the piano and its repertoire are in the spotlight during this year's celebration of Multiple Pianos (9 August). The series also lifts the lid on works to be played by the National Youth Orchestra of Great Britain (8 August) and includes a mouth-watering taster of the Budapest Festival Orchestra with a special family concert designed for 5- to 12-year-olds (18 August). (For *details, see panel, page 73.*)

PROMS SINGING DAY

Although a performance of Handel's *Messiah* leads the way for Proms Singing Day, the young performers involved in Handel's oratorio will not be the only vocal force to raise the Royal Albert Hall roof on 6 September. Families are invited to join some of London's talented youth choirs in a participatory singing event in the afternoon (*see panel, right*), making their collective voices heard in the Royal Albert Hall itself. Proms Plus is working with Sing Up, the Music Manifesto's national singing programme. ●

Andrew Stewart writes on a wide range of classical music and on the music industry. He contributes regularly to *BBC Music Magazine*, *Music Week* and *Classical Music*.

Chris Christodoulou (above left); Simon Jay Price (below right)

'It was the first ever Proms experience for my daughter and me, and – wow – what an introduction! She cannot wait to see the *I Was There* webpage and to hear "our" choir singing away!'

Yvonne and Rebecca Wright (Proms Folk Family Chorus)

Proms Singing day

Royal Albert Hall
Sunday 6 September, 2.00pm–4.00pm
If you love singing and you'd like to come and sing in the Royal Albert Hall, sign up for the Proms Family Chorus on Sunday 6 September. We'll be filling the Royal Albert Hall with hundreds of voices of all ages. Spend the afternoon with Sing Up leaders Sue Hollingworth and Julia Regan. What's more, you'll be recorded by BBC Radio 3. *Free. To book places please visit bbc.co.uk/proms, email promslearning@bbc.co.uk or call 020 7765 0643*

Members of last year's Proms Folk Family Chorus

TRINITY GUILDHALL

A new suite of Certificate Examinations from 1 April 2009
Foundation, Intermediate and Advanced awards in a broad range of instruments.

A new Piano syllabus for 2009
2009-2011 repertoire lists now available.

Trinity Guildhall music qualifications, available in all instruments and voice, cover a variety of styles from classical to contemporary music. With examinations offered at every level – from beginner to accomplished performer – there is something for every musician.

Trinity Guildhall 89 Albert Embankment
London SE1 7TP UK

T +44 (0)20 7820 6100
F +44 (0)20 7820 6161

E music@trinityguildhall.co.uk
www.trinityguildhall.co.uk

TONHALLE ORCHESTRA ZURICH

David Zinman Chief Conductor

PROMS PLUS

Clara Nissen introduces this year's series of talks, discussions, films and other events designed to provide a fresh insight into the music and artists appearing during the Proms season

Last year saw perhaps one of the most significant developments of the past decade at the Proms: the introduction of a pre-concert event before each main evening Prom, spanning a range of formats and providing a fascinating context to the season's music and artists.

Proms Plus this year spreads its wings to the Amaryllis Fleming Concert Hall at the Royal College of Music – with some Proms Family Orchestra events also taking place in other nearby venues – while the series of Proms Films returns to the beautiful space of the Royal Geographical Society (around the corner from the Royal Albert Hall).

Radio 3 listeners can also sample the offerings, with a number of the introductions being broadcast (often during the interval of the relevant Prom). Like the Proms themselves, these will be available via the BBC iPlayer for seven days after broadcast. This year, for the first time, eight events will be webcast on the Proms website and available to watch for the remainder of the season.

Highlights reflecting some of the season's musical threads include a series on Stravinsky ballets, as well as introductions tying in with the four major composer anniversaries (Purcell, Handel, Haydn and Mendelssohn) and with 1934 as a pivotal year for British music. There are also one-off events inspired by the MGM film musicals Prom (1 August) and by our celebration of Multiple Pianos (9 August) and Indian Voices (16 August).

As last year, the series falls into a range of themed categories:

PROMS INTRO

Proms Intros feature conductors, soloists and composers in conversation – or introductions from music experts – sometimes alongside live music. Among this year's highlights are Sir Roger Norrington discussing the impact of Purcell, Handel, Haydn and Mendelssohn (ahead of his Prom on 25 August, in which he conducts the Orchestra of the Age of Enlightenment in music by all four composers); Iván Fischer directing members of his Budapest Festival Orchestra in a special family concert aimed at 5- to 12-year-olds (18 August); and a celebration of the voice with the help of national Singing Ambassador Howard Goodall (introducing Handel's *Messiah* on 6 September). John McCabe and Sir Peter Maxwell Davies also talk about their concertos for horn and violin respectively, which receive their London and UK premieres.

FAMILY MUSIC INTRO *(see also pages 72–79)*

Family Music Intros are a fun and entertaining way for you and your family to find out more about the evening's concert. Aimed at children aged 7-plus, they offer the chance to meet musicians and discover the music featured in the following Proms concert. Bring along your instruments, whatever they are (and whatever your level), if you want to join in. On 27 July there'll also be a special dance-oriented event, in which members of the BBC Symphony Orchestra introduce Stravinsky's ballet *Petrushka* (to be heard that evening).

Family Music Intros are a fun and entertaining way for you and your family to find out more about the evening's concert … Bring along your instruments if you want to join in.

PROMS FAMILY ORCHESTRA *(see also pages 72–79)*

The Proms Family Orchestra gives everyone – regardless of age and ability – the chance to play alongside professional musicians. The result is far from musical mayhem, as proved by the mini-performance at the end of each workshop. This year's workshops include events based around Bollywood (on Indian Voices day) and evolution, as part of the Proms Darwin-anniversary celebrations.

PROMS FILMS

This season sees screenings of eight films and documentaries, among them the classic MGM musical *Singin' in the Rain* and a profile of Daniel Barenboim's boundary-crossing West–Eastern Divan Orchestra, which brings together young Arab and Israeli musicians.

Stan Tracey: The Godfather of British Jazz, 18 July
John Akomfrah's 2003 documentary on the great jazz pianist.

The Birth of British Music, Parts 1 & 2, 25 July
The first two episodes of BBC Two's new major four-part series presented by Charles Hazlewood, focusing respectively on Purcell and Handel.

The Birth of British Music, Parts 3 & 4, 26 July
The conclusion of the BBC Two series, focusing respectively on Haydn and Mendelssohn.

Singin' in the Rain, 1 August
Gene Kelly and Debbie Reynolds star in this iconic MGM musical from 1952.

Diaghilev: The Years Abroad (Part 1); The Years in Exile (Part 2), 8 August
Former Proms Controller John Drummond's 1968 films for the BBC's *Omnibus* series.

Stravinsky: Once, at a Border … , 15 August
Alongside archive footage of the composer himself, family members, colleagues and friends contribute to Tony Palmer's award-winning documentary.

Knowledge is the Beginning, 22 August
Award-winning 2005 documentary by Paul Smaczny on the work of Daniel Barenboim and the West–Eastern Divan Orchestra (in German, with English subtitles).

God Rot Tunbridge Wells, 5 September
Tony Palmer introduces his film on the life of Handel, made to mark the composer's 300th anniversary in 1985. ▶

Top to bottom: *The Birth of British Music, Singin' in the Rain, Knowledge is the Beginning* and *God Rot Tunbridge Wells*

Andy Potts (illustration, p82); BBC ('The Birth of British Music'); MGM/Album/akg-images ('Singin' in the Rain'); Tony Palmer ('God Rot Tunbridge Wells')

AUTUMN 2009 AT ENO

EN O

LE GRAND MACABRE
○ 17 Sep – 9 Oct

TURANDOT
○ 8 Oct – 12 Dec

THE TURN
OF THE SCREW
○ 22 Oct – 7 Nov

DUKE BLUEBEARD'S CASTLE
& THE RITE OF SPRING
○ 6 – 28 Nov

MESSIAH
○ 27 Nov – 11 Dec

ENO Subscribers booking opens 20 April
General booking opens 5 May

ENO LIVE AT THE
LONDON COLISEUM
Book on 0871 911 0200
or at www.eno.org

season sponsor | **skyARTS**

PROMS COMPOSER PORTRAITS

Proms Composer Portraits offer the chance to hear chamber music by four leading composers, each of whom will have a new work premiered at the Royal Albert Hall later the same evening. As well as featuring performances by students from some of the leading British conservatories, the Proms Composer Portrait concerts feature the composer in conversation with Radio 3 presenters Tom Service (29 July, 3 August) and Andrew McGregor (7 August, 9 September). This season's composers are:

Jörg Widmann (29 July) Widmann performs his Fantasie for solo clarinet, alongside performances of Air for solo horn and *Five Fragments* for clarinet and piano.

Michael Jarrell (3 August) Performances to include *Eco* for soprano and piano, *Nachlese II* for violin and cello and *Assonances VII* for percussion.

Louis Andriessen (17 August) Programme includes the UK premiere of *A Very Sad Trumpet Sonata*.

Augusta Read Thomas (9 September) European premieres of *A Circle Around the Sun … for piano trio*, *Invocations* for string quartet and *Passion Prayers* for cello and ensemble.

Clockwise, from top left:
Louis Andriessen, Michael Jarrell, Augusta Read Thomas and Jörg Widmann

Francesca Patella (Andriessen); C. Daguet/Éditions Henry Lemoine, Paris (Jarrell); Don Rest (Thomas)

PROMS LITERARY FESTIVAL

Following its successful debut last year, the Proms Literary Festival again brings together an array of literary figures, from authors and actors to philosophers and historians, to explore the literary and cultural world of which music is a part. In tandem with the Mendelssohn anniversary celebrations, his English contemporaries – the Victorians – form a theme that recurs throughout the festival: Andrew Motion and Fiona Shaw read Tennyson, marking the Victorian poet's bicentenary (2 August); A. N. Wilson (author of *The Victorians*) and Steven Moffat (co-creator of BBC One's new modern-day *Sherlock*) discuss Sherlock Holmes and his special love of Mendelssohn (7 September); and lecturer and G&S enthusiast Ian Bradley delves into the librettos of W. S. Gilbert (11 August).

Other Literary Festival events complementing the Proms season range from Viennese literary culture (Mozart and Mahler, 5 August) to mountain imagery (Strauss's *An Alpine Symphony*, 27 August). Preceding the first of four concerts by the West–Eastern Divan Orchestra, BBC Radio presenter Edward Stourton looks at how the literature of the Middle East has informed his understanding of the region (21 August). Linking together a concert performance of the second act of Birtwistle's *The Mask of Orpheus* and Stravinsky's ballet *Orpheus*, author Philip Pullman examines the Orpheus myth (15 August). Before a performance of Strauss's *Don Quixote*, critic John Mullan talks about the influential legacy of Cervantes's novel, with readings by actor Andrew Sachs (11 September). Many composers through the ages have demonstrated their creativity other than on manuscript paper – proving to be prolific authors in their own right, whether as diarists, poets or letter-writers. Reverend Richard Coles and Janice Galloway – whose novel *Clara* was based on the life of Clara Schumann – discuss the written legacy of such composers. ●

Clara Nissen is Sub-Editor, BBC Proms Publications

For details of all Proms Plus events, please see Listings, pages 105–143

How to Proms Plus

- Proms Plus events are free of charge.
- Most events are held at the Royal College of Music and (except for the First Night's live *In Tune* event) finish one hour before the main evening Prom, allowing you enough time to meet friends or have refreshments before the concert.
- Proms Films take place at the Royal Geographical Society.
- For more information on Proms Family Orchestra workshops, see pages 72–79.
- Prommers who have started queuing for the evening's concert ahead of the Proms Plus event can collect a numbered ticket from one of the Royal Albert Hall stewards, enabling them to retain their place in the Prommers' queue. This is especially advisable for the most popular Proms concerts.
- Events are unticketed – except for the First Night's live *In Tune* event, for which free tickets will be issued (see page 106); seating is unreserved.
- Please note that seating for all Proms Plus events is limited by capacity: we advise arriving early for the more popular events. Doors open 30 minutes before the start-time.
- Since many of the events are recorded for broadcast, latecomers may be admitted only at a suitable break; event stewards will guide you at the appropriate moment.

SHELL CLASSIC INTERNATIONAL
SEP 2009-MAY 2010

GREAT ORCHESTRAS FROM AROUND THE WORLD
ROYAL FESTIVAL HALL

WED 23 SEP 2009, 7.30PM
CHICAGO SYMPHONY ORCHESTRA
Bernard Haitink *conductor*

Mozart Symphony No.41 (Jupiter)
Brahms Symphony No.1

THU 24 SEP 2009, 7.30PM
CHICAGO SYMPHONY ORCHESTRA
Bernard Haitink *conductor*

Haydn Symphony No.101 in D (Clock)
Bruckner Symphony No.7

SAT 28 NOV 2009, 7.30PM
CAMERATA SALZBURG
Leonidas Kavakos *violin, conductor*

Lutosławski Musique funèbre
Bach Violin Concerto in D minor
(reconstructed from Harpsichord
Concerto BWV.1052)
Mozart Symphony No.36 (Linz)

Queen Elizabeth Hall

FRI 29 JAN 2010, 7.30PM
BERLIN STAATSKAPELLE
Daniel Barenboim *piano, conductor*

Beethoven Piano Concerto No.1
Schoenberg Pelleas und Melisande

SUN 31 JAN 2010, 7.45PM
BERLIN STAATSKAPELLE
Daniel Barenboim *piano, conductor*

Schoenberg Verklärte Nacht
Beethoven Piano Concerto No.5
(Emperor)

MON 1 FEB 2010, 7.30PM
BERLIN STAATSKAPELLE
Daniel Barenboim *piano, conductor*

Beethoven Piano Concerto No.2
Schoenberg Five Orchestral Pieces, Op.16
Beethoven Piano Concerto No.4

TUE 2 FEB 2010, 7.30PM
BERLIN STAATSKAPELLE
Daniel Barenboim *piano, conductor*

Programme includes:
Beethoven Piano Concerto No.3
Schoenberg Variations for Orchestra, Op.31

SAT 6 MAR 2010, 7.30PM
**BAVARIAN RADIO SYMPHONY
ORCHESTRA**
Mariss Jansons *conductor*

Programme includes:
Shostakovich Symphony No.10 in E minor

THU 27 MAY 2010, 7.30PM
CHAMBER ORCHESTRA OF EUROPE
Iván Fischer *conductor*
Julia Fischer *violin*

Rossini Overture, The Italian Girl in Algiers
Mendelssohn Violin Concerto
Rossini Variazioni a più istrumenti
obbligati
Schubert Symphony No.5 in B flat

Tickets from £75 - £9

TICKETS 0871 663 2500
WWW.SOUTHBANKCENTRE.CO.UK

SOUTHBANK CENTRE

The reach of the **BBC Proms** has grown significantly in recent years, with more ways to access the performances on **BBC Radio 3, BBC Television** and online. But for more than 75 years the **BBC** has beamed the **Proms** around the world. **Graeme Kay** seeks out who's listening, and who's watching …

FAR AND WIDE

In April 2007 an extraordinary letter turned up at Bush House, headquarters of the BBC World Service. It was the 75th anniversary of the network's first Proms broadcasts, and listeners had been invited to write in with their reminiscences of tuning in under unusual circumstances. Most of us who blithely hit the 'on' button every night during the Proms season may be confident that electricity will be available to power the radio, and that our listening will not be interrupted by incoming artillery shells. Tarik Dreca could take no such thing for granted – tuning in during the three-year siege of Sarajevo in the 1990s required him to shin up an electricity pole every night and drive a screw into a cable used by the United Nations Protection Force peacekeepers; in the early hours he reversed the process before the morning sun revealed his ingenious wire-tap. 'It is difficult for someone who has not experienced life in a besieged city, completely cut off from the outside world, to understand what listening to the Proms meant for me,' Mr Dreca wrote. 'It was a way to escape from everyday ugly reality, a sign of normality in a world gone nuts. It was my own small sign of resistance: even with all their tanks and artillery pieces, they could not prevent me from hearing a work of art, helping me to believe that better times would return one day.'

Ronald Almeida, from Brahmavar, India, didn't have mains power either, but for different reasons. He wrote, simply, 'Listening to the

Great performances, direct to your screen: Daniel Barenboim with the West–Eastern Divan Orchestra at last year's BBC Proms

'It is difficult for someone who has not experienced life in a besieged city, completely cut off from the outside world, to understand what listening to the Proms meant for me.'

Tarik Dreca, from Sarajevo

BBC Proms on my portable radio, in a little village in the middle of the jungle without electricity under a starry sky, will always be a memorable experience for me.' Gladys S. Kothavala, in Pune, India, had heard a Proms broadcast of *The Trojans* in 1982: 'I wonder what Berlioz would have produced if he could have heard local and modern Tunisian music,' she enquired.

In *The Proms: A New History* (2007) David Wright noted that 'World Service felt broadcasting a selection of Proms was an important part of their remit, and received more letters about them than about any other concerts they transmitted'. Though the incoming

correspondence attests to the value that overseas viewers and listeners place on the Proms, working out how many of them are tuning in is more problematic. While UK audiences are calculated for TV by the Broadcasting Audience Research Board (BARB) and for radio by RAJAR (Radio Joint Audience Research), international figures can only be guesstimates based on the catchment areas of the various receiving stations. But we are talking many hundreds of millions here.

So who, and where, are the Proms's international broadcast partners? A look at the 2008 season provides a sample. Thirteen concerts were released by BBC Worldwide to radio stations in Australia, Spain, the Cayman Islands, Norway, Qatar, Hong Kong and Sweden. The programmes on offer reflected the innate diversity of the Proms, ranging from Renaissance masterpieces with The Tallis Scholars to Handel's *Belshazzar*, Messiaen's *La Transfiguration de Notre Seigneur Jésus-Christ* and the Berlin Philharmonic performing Shostakovich. The Last Night of the Proms was taken up by TV stations in Japan, Germany, Sweden, Norway, Belgium and Australia. BBC Radio 3 estimates that in an average year there are 1,000 concert broadcasts of music from the Proms season, via its European Broadcasting Union partners.

So popular is the Last Night on radio throughout the world that broadcasters in China, Germany, Portugal and the USA send announcers to cover the event live or 'recorded-as-live', making the corridor outside Loggia Box 3 at the Royal Albert Hall the World ▶

Chris Christodoulou (p88 & above right)

On air: Sean Rafferty and guest presenter, former yachtswoman Clare Francis, in the Radio 3 presenter's box during the Last Night of the Proms 2008

The Proms on BBC Radio 3

- BBC Proms broadcast live on BBC Radio 3 (90–93FM)
- Many Proms repeated during *Afternoon on 3* (weekdays, 2.00pm), plus a series of repeats over the Christmas period
- Listen Again for seven days after broadcast via the BBC iPlayer
- Proms-related programmes during the season on *Breakfast* (every day, 7.00am), *In Tune* (weekdays, 5.00pm) and *Summer CD Review* (Saturdays, 9.00am)

The Proms on BBC World Service

- Highlights from 10 Proms on BBC World Service in English, on SW, FM, DAB and DRM (for details, see www.bbc.co.uk/worldservice)
- Further Proms broadcasts in Mandarin on the BBC Chinese Service
- Interviews with Proms artists on *The Strand*, the World Service's daily arts programme
- Last Night of the Proms live on BBC World Service on DRM, as well as Antena 2 (Portugal), APM (USA) and other stations

Service nerve centre – a lively, polyglot place to be during rehearsal breaks. And the mere mention of audiences in China and the USA suggests an aggregated potential audience adding up to many millions.

A key figure in the international planning of the Proms is World Service producer Radek Boschetty. 'There have been Proms on the World Service since 1932,' he explains. 'Currently we have about 11 concerts on the English service and five on the Chinese during the season; occasionally other services take Proms, including the Russian and Arabic. Producing the concerts is a jigsaw. With the exception of the Last Night, all of the concerts are edited into 53-minute packages; this can create repertoire difficulties as each package has to make sense artistically. In terms of presentation, you can address audiences in, for example, Australia, the USA, Nigeria, Kenya and Singapore as you would a UK audience that is familiar with classical music. But outside the West, or Western-influenced countries, you have to supply more of the context – to explain without being patronising.'

Boschetty continues, 'As a producer, I don't have an entirely free hand with the packaging of the programmes, because I'm working within certain limitations of the World Service airwaves. About half of the World Service is on Short Wave and half on FM; although FM is growing, I still have to bear in mind that some Short Wave listeners experience sound which, of its nature, isn't of the highest quality, but which is definitely not worse than listening on a poor internet connection. For example, you can't have any music that is too quiet for too long, otherwise the SW transmitters could think that the output had ceased and turn themselves off! One reason why we've

Lily Feng (right), BBC Chinese Service, with Gu Yue from Beijing Music Radio

never broadcast Holst's *The Planets* is because of all the extremely quiet passages – which is a shame.

'It's a challenging facet of the work, and one which staff producing for the UK audience don't have to think about. The other main challenge is the turnaround – because of World Service time zones, we're often up all night editing our concert packages together – 5.00am for us is early evening in New Zealand, a good time for a concert and

> 'The other main challenge is the turnaround – because of World Service time zones, we're often up all night editing our concert packages together.'
>
> World Service producer Radek Boschetty

you don't want to let things slip by a day for those listeners furthest forward of Greenwich Mean Time as they would lose the sense of actuality.'

International listeners with reception difficulties may take comfort from the fact that a replacement for Short Wave is advancing over the horizon: DRM (Digital Radio Mondiale) is the SW equivalent of Digital Audio Broadcasting (DAB). 'We had our first stereo music broadcast on DRM in 2007,' explains Boschetty, 'and now the Last Night is available live only via DRM.'

The BBC's Chinese Service is an important client of the Proms because of the huge interest in classical music within China. Features editor Lu Jiang tells me that, in 2008, the Service covered five Proms, plus the world premiere of Chen Yi's BBC-commissioned *Olympic Fire*, and the Radio 3 Awards for World Music Prom, which featured Sa Dingding, the Chinese winner of the Awards' Asian category. 'Shanghai East Radio sent over two people to join us for the coverage of two concerts,' notes Jiang, 'and Beijing Music Radio rebroadcast our programmes through its satellite network, linking 22 stations across China – other partners include Yunnan, Hebei and Hainan Radio stations. We've been doing this for five years and, as well as satisfying the thirst of Chinese people to hear the best

Chris Christodoulou (top left)

17:49:28

patriotic, that
exhorts us to
create in this
country a place
of universal

Chris Christodoulou (main image & inset)

orchestras in the best classical music, it also raises
the BBC's profile. In our first year, the Minister of
Communication in Beijing heard a concert and phoned
the Managing Director of our partner broadcaster to say,
"You must do more of this!"'

In Loggia Box 3, Chinese Service presenter Lily Feng
is joined by presenters from the receiving stations, and by
their very own pundit, Professor Cao Quin, Director of
International Development at the East Coast Music
Academy in Grimsby. 'We provide our guest presenters
with all the necessary presentation notes,' says Lily.
'Although we're all very experienced, we have our
moments, such as when there was an unannounced
encore and none of us – not even the Professor – knew

what it was. I quickly passed a note round the pillar to
the Radio 3 box next door and they kindly scribbled down
the name of the piece, so by the time our microphones
went live again we knew what to say!'

Further down the Loggia corridor on my visit during
the 2008 Last Night, other teams of overseas presenters are
preparing their scripts: in Box 32, the avuncular Anglophile
journalist and film-maker Rolf Seelmann-Eggebert shares the
party atmosphere with listeners in Germany; I meet Luis
Caetano of Portuguese Public Radio, who tells me, 'On my
station, Antena 2, we have a smattering of live concerts
during the year and we've been taking the Last Night of
the Proms since 2000. The public appreciates the quality of
the music and the freedom the musicians have to express ▶

The Proms on BBC Television

- 25 Proms broadcast across BBC One, BBC Two, BBC Four and BBC HD
- Regular Saturday-evening broadcasts on BBC Two
- Regular Thursday- and Friday-evening coverage on BBC Four
- New Maestro Cam, along with expert audio commentary, available for five Proms via the red button
- Take your seat for the Last Night of the Proms (first half on BBC Two and second half on BBC One) – plus Proms in the Park events around the country via the red button

Talented? Your future is mada.

Chetham's School of Music, Manchester

Elmhurst School for Dance, Birmingham

St Mary's Music School, Edinburgh

The Hammond School, Chester

The Purcell School for Young Musicians , Hertfordshire

The Royal Ballet School, London

Tring Park School for the Performing Arts, Hertfordshire

Wells Cathedral School, Somerset

- Government funding (up to 100%) available:
    - www.dcsf.gov.uk/mds
    - www.scotland.gov.uk/topics/education/schools/excellence
- Committed to the highest teaching standards in Music & Dance
- Committed to an excellent academic education

THE 9 SCHOOLS OF
MUSIC AND DANCE mada

themselves. Young people who like classical music tell us they want to have something like the Last Night in Portugal – from our point of view it accords classical music the place it deserves, which is as a popular, not an elitist, art form.'

Minnesota-based American Public Media has sent over producer Brad Althoff and Brian Newhouse, a Peabody Prize-winning presenter. 'The Last Night goes out in a strand called *Performance Today*,' says Newhouse. 'The term "Proms" is a mystery to Americans – to us, a Prom is a high-school junior dance. Now there's a glimmer of awareness starting: New York and Los Angeles are taking the concert now. Of course, it's a wonderful occasion, which makes great radio. Even the British national anthem has resonance because the tune is familiar to us – but to different words – as the patriotic song "America". The audience has become engaged, and it runs into several millions now, which is great.'

The reaction of overseas listeners to the Proms can readily be understood from the correspondence: it evokes the shared enthusiasm for the quality of the music-making

> 'Japanese people … respect the cultural climate that makes an event such as the Last Night possible.'
>
> Professor Kazuyoshi Nakaya, Tokyo University

and the accessibility of the event. In a recent Radio 4 documentary, Hansjurg Fuchs of the Bayreuth Anglo-German Society explained to journalist John F. Jungclaussen precisely why Germans love the Last Night enough to stage their own version of it in Hamburg every year. 'Don't forget that culturally we are linked to Britain through Romanticism; Walter Scott, Wordsworth and Turner have their counterpart in the work of Caspar David Friedrich. Romanticism swept from the highlands of Scotland deep into the Black Forest. That's a tradition, but the difference is that you have a more relaxed attitude to your traditions in England. It can be fun – horrendous fun; fun and ridiculous.'

And Professor Kazuyoshi Nakaya of Tokyo University offered me the following insights from Japan, where the Last Night is broadcast on the NHK BS channel. 'It is regarded as unique rather than eccentric. All of the Proms have a style that you cannot find anywhere else in the world. Japanese people are very envious of this and, in a sense, respect the cultural climate that makes an event such as the Last Night possible. We admire the opportunity the Prommers have to participate actively in a classical music concert. Given the sensitivities surrounding Japan's national anthem [it was discarded after the Second World War and reinstated in 1999], we envy the British people, who can sing patriotic music so spontaneously, and the freedom which allows it. After all, it is music, not political slogans.'

Audience engagement of this kind has been characteristic of the BBC Proms overseas broadcasts since the beginning. And, if anything ever goes wrong, the staff can expect to be told in no uncertain terms to pull their socks up. This comment, from Corporal A. Sunnucks of the Mediterranean Station, Malta, was received in 1946, but it might have been yesterday: 'We had several Promenade Concerts and each time you have most unkindly cut us off right in the middle of the last movement. In no instance has the following programme been one that could not have been either put back or scrapped altogether.' Ouch! Well, that was 60 years ago. Were he tuning in to the Proms today, Corporal Sunnucks would no doubt be impressed that his commitment as a listener is mirrored by a growing worldwide audience, served by the many broadcast platforms offered in this digital age. ●

Graeme Kay is an Interactive Producer for BBC Audio and Music, and former Editor of *BBC Music Magazine*.

The Proms Online

- Experience the festival blog: a living scrapbook of the latest Proms and Radio 3 activity
- Regular contributions from Roger Wright and the Proms production team
- Every Prom available online
- Exclusive videos of Proms talks and interviews
- Comprehensive programme notes for every concert
- Proms news via the web and mobile WAP sites
- Daily text alerts to keep you up to date
- Send reviews via SMS or email to be shared on Radio 3's *Breakfast* show every morning
- Weekly podcasts from Radio 3's *In Tune*: interviews with Proms performers, conductors and composers

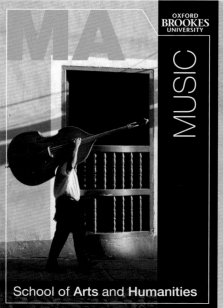
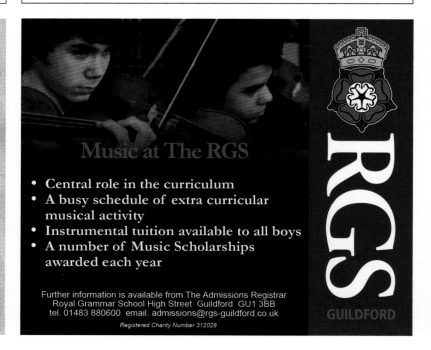

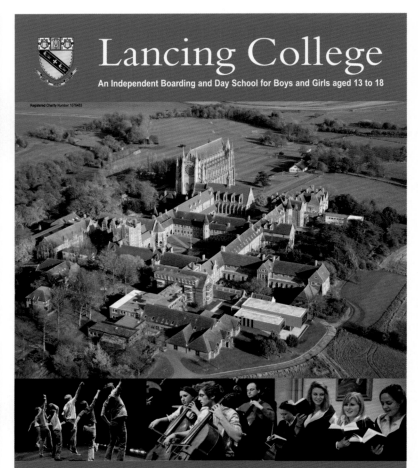

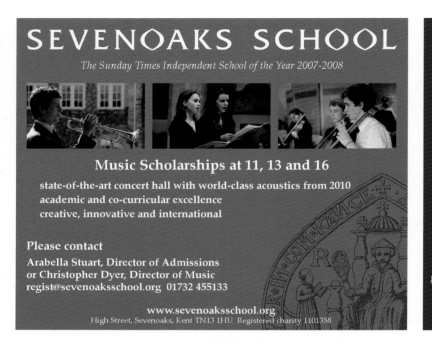

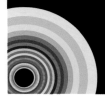

PIERINO
PASTA PIZZA RESTAURANT
37 THURLOE PLACE, LONDON SW7 2HP

Telephone 020 7581 3770

Monday to Friday 12–3.00pm, 5.30–11.30pm

Saturday & Sunday 12 noon–11.30pm

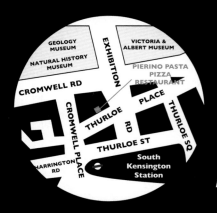

Prompt service guaranteed for you to be in time for the performance.

We are within walking distance of the Royal Albert Hall, near South Kensington tube station.

You are welcome before and after the performance.

EXPERIENCE OF SERVING GENUINE ITALIAN FOOD AND FOR
HOME-MADE PASTA AND THE BEST PIZZA IN LONDON

30 YEARS

CONCERT LISTINGS

ADVANCE BOOKING

Online and by post
Monday 20 April – Monday 18 May

GENERAL BOOKING

Online, by post and in person from Tuesday 26 May

Online: bbc.co.uk/proms
Telephone: 0845 401 5040*

For full booking information and the Advance Booking Form, see pages 146–153

PRICE CODES

A ▼ G Each concert at the Royal Albert Hall falls into one of seven price bands, colour-coded for ease of reference. For full list of prices, see page 151. For special offers, see page 148.

NB: concert start-times vary across the season – check before you book

All concert details were correct at the time of going to press. The BBC reserves the right to alter artist or programme details as necessary.

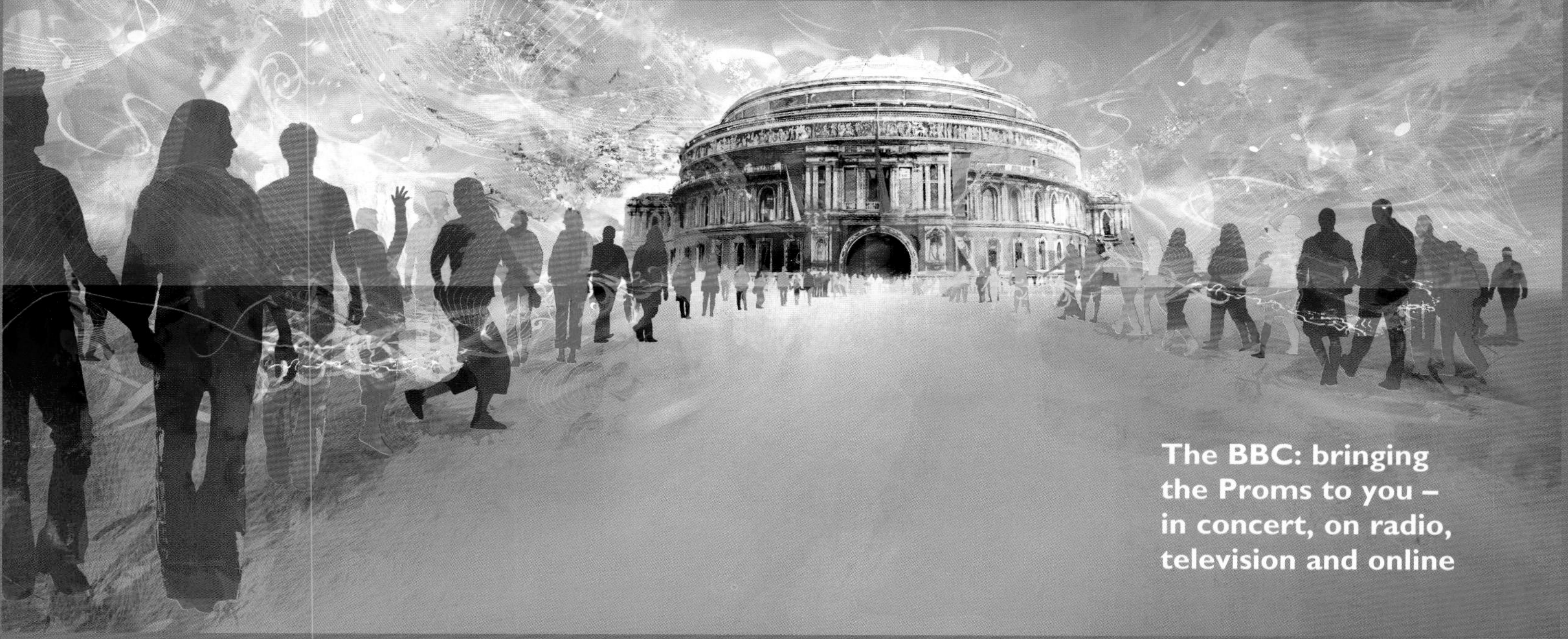

The BBC: bringing the Proms to you – in concert, on radio, television and online

**Calls cost up to 4p/min from a BT landline (plus a one-off connection charge of up to 8p). Charges from mobiles and other networks may be considerably higher*

WEEKEND PROMMING PASS • BEAT THE QUEUES AND SAVE MONEY (SEE PAGE 148)

FRIDAY 17 JULY

Proms Plus 5.00pm, Royal College of Music
In Tune Sean Rafferty and Petroc Trelawny present a special edition of BBC Radio 3's *In Tune*, featuring Proms artists, music from the season and a preview of the Proms Literary Festival.
Tickets available from BBC Audience Services (bbc.co.uk/tickets)

7.30pm–c10.20pm

Stravinsky
Fireworks   *4'*

Chabrier
Ode à la musique   *9'*

Tchaikovsky
Piano Concerto No. 3 in E flat major   *16'*

interval

Poulenc
Concerto for two pianos   *20'*

interval

Elgar
In the South (Alassio)   *22'*

Brahms
Alto Rhapsody   *13'*

Bruckner
Psalm 150   *9'*

Ailish Tynan *soprano*
Alice Coote *mezzo-soprano*
Stephen Hough *piano*
Katia and Marielle Labèque *pianos*

BBC Symphony Chorus
BBC Symphony Orchestra
Jiří Bělohlávek *conductor*

An exciting mix to open the 2009 Proms. We launch our celebrations of Stravinsky, Tchaikovsky, Multiple Pianos and more. Two starry former BBC Radio 3 New Generation Artists mark the scheme's 10th anniversary, and all of tonight's soloists return later in the season.

Broadcast
RADIO Live on Radio 3
ONLINE Live and 'listen again' options at bbc.co.uk/proms
TV Broadcast at 8.00pm on BBC Two

SATURDAY 18 JULY

Proms Plus
2.00pm, Royal Geographical Society **Film** *Stan Tracey: The Godfather of British Jazz* (70', awaiting classification). A portrait of the jazz legend, introduced by Geoffrey Smith.
5.15pm, Royal College of Music **Proms Intro** Louise Fryer is joined by David Wyn Jones (Cardiff University) and conductor/musicologist Denis McCaldin to introduce Haydn's *The Creation*.

7.00pm–c9.00pm

Haydn
The Creation   *109'*
(sung in English, with revised text by Paul McCreesh)

Rosemary Joshua *Gabriel*
Sarah Tynan *Eve*
Mark Padmore *Uriel*
Neal Davies *Raphael*
Peter Harvey *Adam*

Chetham's Chamber Choir
Gabrieli Consort & Players
Paul McCreesh *conductor*

What more natural selection with which to launch our 'Creation'-themed first Saturday, and to mark the joint anniversaries of Haydn and Darwin (the latter born in 1809, the year of the former's death). Haydn's Handel-inspired hymn to God's 'glorious work' burst into life 50 years before Darwin's *On the Origin of Species*, but its masterly depiction of each new-created phenomenon – from blinding first light through primordial chaos to the arrival of mankind – has proved no mere seven-days'-wonder. Paul McCreesh conducts massed Gabrieli forces in a recreation of the giant versions that Haydn himself directed in the last decade of his life. Celebrating 40 years as a music school, Chetham's sends its chamber choir to swell the vocal ranks. Mark Padmore and Neal Davies return later in the season for Handel's *Samson* (Prom 47). See *'Composers of the Year'*, pages 28–33

There will be no interval

Rosemary Joshua

PROM 2
Spotlight on … Paul McCreesh

It may be Haydn's best-known oratorio, but Paul McCreesh is bringing to the Proms a *Creation* with a difference. Not only is he deploying unusually large – though historically authentic – period-instrument forces, he has also reworked the English text. 'The libretto in English is difficult to interpret,' believes McCreesh, 'and Haydn clearly wanted the immediacy of the performance in a vernacular tongue. So, using original sources, I made a new translation which is more singable and, I think, as good as the German. It took two years, with many late-night text messages to singers, asking "Can you think of a three-syllable word meaning – ?"'

'There's a sort of universal validity about this story that transcends religious views. In a sense, this great oratorio heralds a new age – it was written at the dawn of the industrial age, and only a few years after the French Revolution. *The Creation* reaffirmed old traditions when the world seemed new and frightening.'

Joining the Gabrieli Consort & Players at the Proms are choral forces from Manchester's Chetham's School of Music. 'As with so many young people,' McCreesh says, 'the higher the standards, the higher they jump. I certainly learn as much as they do.'

SAME-DAY SAVER
Book for both Proms 2 and 3 and save (see page 148)

Broadcast
RADIO Live on Radio 3
ONLINE Live and 'listen again' options at bbc.co.uk/proms

SATURDAY 18 JULY

10.15pm–c11.15pm

Stan Tracey and his Orchestra

Stan Tracey

Genesis *c50'*

Almost two centuries after Haydn celebrated God's 'glorious work' in *The Creation* (Prom 2), living legend Stan Tracey – known to his fans as the 'Godfather of British jazz' – also went back to the beginning, brilliantly recreating the biblical version of the Big Bang as a Big Band suite. Now the former Ted Heath Orchestra member and longtime resident pianist at Ronnie Scott's brings his 1987 ode to creation to the Proms for the first time.

There will be no interval

Stan Tracey

SAME-DAY SAVER
Book for both Proms 2 and 3 and save (see page 148)

SUNDAY 19 JULY

Proms Plus 4.15pm, Royal College of Music
Proms Intro Tonight's conductor Lars Ulrik Mortensen and Dr Suzanne Aspden (University of Oxford) join Catherine Bott to introduce Handel's *Partenope*.
Edited version broadcast on Radio 3 during tonight's first interval

6.00pm–c10.05pm

Handel

Partenope *c180'*
(concert performance; sung in Italian)

Inger Dam-Jensen *Partenope*
Tuva Semmingsen *Rosmira*
Andreas Scholl *Arsace*
Christophe Dumaux *Armindo*
Bo Kristian Jensen *Emilio*
Palle Knudsen *Ormonte*

Concerto Copenhagen
Lars Ulrik Mortensen *conductor*

Andreas Scholl

Handel's posthumous fame long rested on his sacred oratorios such as *Samson* (Prom 47) and *Messiah* (Prom 68), but it was as a master of Italian opera that he ruled the London stage for over two decades. His many operas are distinguished by unforgettable melodies, inimitable invention and a Shakespearean breadth of human sympathies (and all are being broadcast on BBC Radio 3 during the course of this year). A relative rarity even today, when Handel's operas are once again back at the heart of the core repertoire, *Partenope* is a dazzling comic parody of a typical *opera seria* plot, which only unravels when the supposed Prince of Armenia is challenged to fight bare-chested – and so is exposed as the disguised Rosmira, her challenger's abandoned fiancée. For its first complete Proms performance, the cast of the Royal Danish Opera's new production, conducted by period specialist Lars Ulrik Mortensen, is led by 1993 Cardiff Singer of the World, Inger Dam-Jensen, and star counter-tenor Andreas Scholl. See 'Composers of the Year', pages 28–33

There will be two intervals

William Ellis (Tracey); Eric Larrayadieu (Scholl); Thomas Petri/Royal Danish Opera (Partenope production, 2008)

MONDAY 20 JULY

1.00pm–c2.00pm

Proms Chamber Music at Cadogan Hall

Henry VIII
Pastyme with good companye 2'

Fayrfax
Missa 'Regali ex progenie' – Gloria 9'

W. Cornysh
Ah, Robin, gentle Robin 4'

Henry VIII
Hélas, madame 2'

Fayrfax
Benedicite! What dreamed I? 3'

Sampson
Psallite felices 10'

Taverner
Christe Jesu, pastor bone 3'

Tallis
Sancte Deus, sancte fortis 6'

Ludford
Domine Jesu Christe 10'

The Cardinall's Musick
Andrew Carwood director

Andrew Carwood and his vocal ensemble launch the Proms Chamber Music series by marking the 500th anniversary of the coronation of Henry VIII. Richly sonorous and grand in design, the music of the time combines massive choral writing with a complex layering of solo lines. The programme's mix of sacred and secular includes songs by King Henry himself, and settings of texts in his honour by leading composers of the day.

There will be no interval

Broadcast
RADIO Live on Radio 3
ONLINE Live and 'listen again' options at bbc.co.uk/proms

MONDAY 20 JULY

Proms Plus 5.15pm, Royal College of Music
Proms Intro Stephen Johnson talks to author and lecturer Jeremy Barham and composer David Matthews about Mahler's Symphony No. 9.

7.00pm–c8.30pm

Mahler
Symphony No. 9 85'

London Symphony Orchestra
Bernard Haitink conductor

Begun in the summer of 1909, Mahler's last completed symphony was written at a time of crisis, following the loss of a daughter, his forced resignation from the Vienna Court Opera, the diagnosis of his own fatal heart disease and the breakdown of his marriage. Yet, while the first movement is permeated by premonitions of death and the last fades away into nothingness, the enduring impression is one of resigned, even joyful acceptance of man's fate. One of the world's great Mahlerians, Bernard Haitink this year celebrates both his 80th birthday and the 50th anniversary of his UK debut.

There will be no interval

Bernard Haitink

SAME-DAY SAVER Book for both Proms 5 and 6 and save (see page 148)

Broadcast
RADIO Live on Radio 3
ONLINE Live and 'listen again' options at bbc.co.uk/proms

MONDAY 20 JULY

9.30pm–c11.30pm

Haydn
The Seven Last Words of Our Saviour on the Cross 62'

James MacMillan
Seven Last Words from the Cross 44'

Elizabeth Watts soprano
Renata Pokupić mezzo-soprano
James Gilchrist tenor
Darren Jeffery bass-baritone

BBC Singers
Manchester Camerata
Douglas Boyd conductor

Douglas Boyd

Haydn's *Seven Last Words* – 'seven sonatas with an introduction and a concluding earthquake' – were commissioned by Cadiz Cathedral for performance on Good Friday 1786. Haydn regarded these orchestral meditations upon Christ's Crucifixion as among his most successful works; he quickly arranged the music for piano and string quartet, and later adapted it as a cantata just before starting work on *The Creation* (Prom 2). Two centuries later, James MacMillan's *Seven Last Words* was commissioned by BBC Television and shown in nightly instalments during Holy Week 1994. Revived to mark the composer's 50th birthday, this powerfully dramatic cantata is underscored by echoes of plainsong, Bach chorales and traditional Scottish laments. See 'Composers of the Year', pages 28–33; 'Bright Young Things', pages 48–51

There will be no interval

Broadcast
RADIO Live on Radio 3
ONLINE Live and 'listen again' options at bbc.co.uk/proms

Matthias Creutziger (Haitink) John Batten (Boyd)

TUESDAY 21 JULY

Proms Plus 4.45pm, Royal College of Music
Proms Literary Festival Historian Alison Weir and critic John Carey explore the myth and reality of Elizabeth I, the monarch who inspired Spenser's *The Faerie Queene*. Rana Mitter presents.
Edited version broadcast on Radio 3 during tonight's interval

6.30pm–c10.15pm

Purcell
The Fairy Queen *(semi-staged)*   c180'

Glyndebourne Festival Opera

Cast to include:
Lucy Crowe soprano
Claire Debono soprano
Anna Devin soprano
Carolyn Sampson soprano
Robert Burt tenor
Ed Lyon tenor
Andrew Foster-Williams bass-baritone

Glyndebourne Chorus
Orchestra of the Age of Enlightenment
William Christie conductor

Purcell's most lavish theatre score launches our celebration marking the 350th anniversary of his birth. Devised to accompany a cut-down version of Shakespeare's *A Midsummer Night's Dream* – and omitting all the scenes that fellow anniversarian Felix Mendelssohn set to music 150 years later (Prom 72) – this 'semi-opera' takes the form of a series of fantastical masques presented for the entertainment of Titania, Oberon and their fairy court. Baroque master William Christie presides over a semi-staging of this summer's new production by Glyndebourne Festival Opera, celebrating its 75th anniversary this year. See 'Composers of the Year', pages 28–33

There will be one interval

Broadcast
RADIO Live on Radio 3
ONLINE Live and 'listen again' options at bbc.co.uk/proms

WEDNESDAY 22 JULY

Proms Plus 6.15pm, Royal College of Music
Proms Intro To celebrate the 800th anniversary of the University of Cambridge, Louise Fryer hosts a discussion with past and present Directors of Music at King's College – Sir David Willcocks and Stephen Cleobury – alongside Nicholas Cook, Professor of Music, University of Cambridge and composer Ryan Wigglesworth.
Edited version broadcast on Radio 3 during tonight's interval

8.00pm–c10.30pm

Vaughan Williams
The Wasps – Overture   9'

Ryan Wigglesworth
The Genesis of Secrecy   c10'
BBC commission: world premiere

Vaughan Williams
Five Mystical Songs   18'

interval

Stanford
Magnificat and Nunc dimittis in A major   12'

Jonathan Harvey
Come, Holy Ghost*   7'

Judith Weir
Ascending into Heaven†   8'

Saint-Saëns
Symphony No. 3, 'Organ'   36'

Simon Keenlyside baritone
Thomas Trotter organ

Choirs of King's and St John's colleges
Choirs of Clare, Gonville and Caius, and Trinity colleges
Choirs from combined Cambridge colleges
BBC Symphony Orchestra
Sir Andrew Davis conductor
Stephen Cleobury† conductor
Andrew Nethsingha* conductor

King's College, Cambridge

We celebrate the 800th anniversary of the University of Cambridge with a concert given by a convocation of the university's college choirs and two soloists and a conductor who are among its graduates. As Professor of Music, Stanford taught Vaughan Williams, who wrote his *Wasps* overture for a university staging of Aristophanes' comedy, and later set verses by a former University Orator, George Herbert, in his *Five Mystical Songs*. Jonathan Harvey – who this year celebrates his 70th birthday – and Judith Weir also studied at Cambridge. Ryan Wigglesworth went to Oxford but is now a Cambridge lecturer and fellow of Corpus Christi College: in a Proms double debut this season, he returns to co-conduct the BBC SO in Prom 39. Saint-Saëns was awarded an honorary doctorate by the university in 1893. See 'New Music', pages 54–60

Sir Andrew Davis

Simon Keenlyside

Broadcast
RADIO Live on Radio 3
ONLINE Live and 'listen again' options at bbc.co.uk/proms

THURSDAY 23 JULY

Proms Plus 5.45pm, Royal College of Music
Proms Intro Rob Cowan discusses British music with writer-broadcasters Stephen Johnson and Piers Burton-Page.

7.30pm–c10.05pm

Moeran
Symphony in G minor 45'

Finzi
Grand Fantasia and Toccata 15'

interval

Elgar
Symphony No. 2 in E flat major 55'

Leon McCawley *piano*

BBC Philharmonic
Vassily Sinaisky *conductor*

Vassily Sinaisky, the BBC Philharmonic's Chief Guest Conductor, enjoys exploring the less-frequented byways of the English repertoire. E. J. Moeran's Symphony, introduced to the Proms in 1938 by founder-conductor Henry Wood, was written partly in Norfolk, partly in County Kerry, and seems to evoke the landscapes, seashores and folk idioms of both (though train buffs also claim to be able to hear echoes of the Great Eastern expresses). Finzi's neo-Classical Grand Fantasia caps an unaccompanied and clearly Bach-inspired piano solo with a jaunty, finger-tapping Toccata. And we mark the 75th-anniversary of Elgar's death with his Second Symphony, a nobly expansive exploration of past sorrows recalled and exorcised. See *'England at the Crossroads'*, pages 36–38

Vassily Sinaisky

Broadcast
RADIO Live on Radio 3
ONLINE Live and 'listen again' options at bbc.co.uk/proms
TV Live on BBC Four

FRIDAY 24 JULY

Proms Plus 5.45pm, Royal College of Music
Proms Intro Conductor Jun Märkl and shō player Mayumi Miyata talk to Tom Service about tonight's programme.

7.30pm–c10.25pm

Takemitsu
Ceremonial: An Autumn Ode 8'

Debussy, orch. Caplet
Estampes – Pagodes 8'

Ravel
Rapsodie espagnole 16'

interval

Takemitsu
Green 6'

Sarasate
'Carmen' Fantasy 12'

Ravel
Tzigane 10'

interval

Toshio Hosokawa
Cloud and Light 17'
UK premiere

Debussy
La mer 25'

Akiko Suwanai *violin*
Mayumi Miyata *shō*

Orchestre National de Lyon
Jun Märkl *conductor*

Mayumi Miyata

Half-German, half-Japanese, Jun Märkl conducts a French orchestra in a three-part Prom tracing musical cross-fertilisations between East and West, and between France and Spain. Takemitsu's *Ceremonial* showcases the Japanese shō (mouth organ) but the key influence on his *Green* was Debussy – who had himself used oriental scales and sonorities in 'Pagodes' and *La mer*. The shō reappears in Hosokawa's recent *Cloud and Light*, which, despite its Debussyan title, was inspired by an image of the Buddha. Bizet never visited Spain but even real Spaniards such as Sarasate adored his *Carmen*; Ravel, by contrast, imbibed a love of Spain from his Basque mother, though the gypsy of his *Tzigane* is clearly Hungarian. The youngest ever winner of the International Tchaikovsky Competition, Akiko Suwanai made her Proms debut last year in Peter Eötvös's concerto *Seven*. See *'New Music'*, pages 54–60

PROM 10
Spotlight on ... Jun Märkl

The idea for this French–Japanese programme came about prior to a tour of Japan by conductor Jun Märkl and his Orchestre National de Lyon. 'I wanted to document the strong relationship of the arts between these two countries, and also to introduce traditional Japanese instruments.' Both Takemitsu and Hosokawa have combined Eastern and Western traditions in writing music for shō and orchestra, leading to the unusual appearance of the Japanese instrument – a bamboo-piped mouth organ traditionally used in Japanese court music – at the Proms.

The French element of the programme sits remarkable naturally alongside the Japanese. 'As Debussy was writing *La mer*,' Märkl explains, 'he had a Japanese woodblock print of a wave in his study, a clear sign that French composers were influenced by the Japanese arts.'

Broadcast
RADIO Live on Radio 3
ONLINE Live and 'listen again' options at bbc.co.uk/proms
TV Live on BBC Four

SATURDAY 25 JULY

5.00pm–c6.05pm

Elgar, arr. Atkins
Organ Sonata No. 2   *15'*

Peter Dickinson
Blue Rose Variations   *15'*

Elgar
Organ Sonata No. 1 in G major   *25'*

David Titterington *organ*

David Titterington

Launching a weekend marking 75 years since the deaths of Delius, Elgar and Holst in 1934, David Titterington takes to the Royal Albert Hall's 'Father' Willis organ to perform the grand, quasi-symphonic Sonata that the Worcester-born Elgar composed in 1895 for the Cathedral's new organist, Hugh Blair, to play for a group of visiting Americans. The so-called Second Sonata is in fact a free transcription by Ivor Atkins (Blair's longer-lasting successor) of the *Severn Suite* which, in 1930, the elderly Elgar nostalgically worked up from youthful sketches, including musical depictions of Worcester's Cathedral and Castle. The transatlantic connection is continued in Peter Dickinson's *Blue Rose Variations*, in which the British composer and American music expert – born in the year of Elgar's death – takes a famous tune by Edward MacDowell and gives it a blues and ragtime spin. *See 'England at the Crossroads', pages 36–38*

There will be no interval

Broadcast
RADIO Live on Radio 3
ONLINE Live and 'listen again' options at bbc.co.uk/proms

SATURDAY 25 JULY

7.30pm–c9.40pm

Elgar
Overture 'Cockaigne (In London Town)'   *13'*

Delius
The Song of the High Hills   *28'*

interval

Holst
The Planets   *50'*

Rebecca Evans *soprano*
Toby Spence *tenor*

BBC Singers
BBC Philharmonic
Sir Charles Mackerras *conductor*

In the second of this weekend's concerts celebrating the musical legacy of the three great British composers who died 75 years ago, Sir Charles Mackerras contrasts Elgar's 'stout and steaky' salute to the indomitable Cockney spirit of old London Town with Delius's poetical evocation of 'the joy and exhilaration one feels in the mountains … and the grandeur of the wide, far distances', before venturing into the solar system for Holst's mystical planetary survey – which, like Delius's hilltop song, memorably deploys a wordless chorus to ethereal effect. *See 'England at the Crossroads', pages 36–38*

SAME-DAY SAVER
Book for both Proms 11 and 12 and save (see page 148)

Broadcast
RADIO Live on Radio 3
ONLINE Live and 'listen again' options at bbc.co.uk/proms
TV Broadcast at 8.00pm on BBC Two (with Maestro Cam via red button)

PROM 12
Spotlight on ... Sir Charles Mackerras

Though born in New York and brought up in Australia, Sir Charles Mackerras has been a devoted champion of British music throughout his distinguished career.

A celebrated interpreter of the operettas of Gilbert & Sullivan – whose *Patience* he returns to conduct in Prom 35 – he is equally steeped in British music of the 20th century, making him an ideal figure to grace this year's Proms celebration of three great British composers who all died in 1934: Delius, Elgar and Holst.

Though all three pieces in tonight's Prom were written within the first 20 years of the last century, they contrast widely in mood and subject. 'Delius's *The Song of the High Hills* is a nature piece,' explains Mackerras – 'it's an impression of the solitude of Norwegian mountains and fjords. The wordless choir comes in so gently, you're not sure whether you've heard it right! Elgar's *Cockaigne* is a jolly overture about London. He represents all the various sounds you can hear in the city – the Cockney whistle, brass bands and church bells.' Meanwhile, Mackerras regards Holst's *The Planets* as 'a pioneering piece, particularly in its orchestral colouring and unusual instruments, such as the tenor tuba, bass oboe and alto flute. It's rightly one of the most famous pieces in the whole orchestral repertoire.'

SUNDAY 26 JULY

11.00am–c1.00pm

FREE Family Prom

Khachaturian
Gayane – Sabre Dance   *3'*

Chopin, orch. Stravinsky
Waltz in E flat major, Op. 18
'Grande valse brillante'   *6'*

Sir Richard Rodney Bennett
Lilliburlero Variations   *10'*
world premiere of orchestral version

Holst
A Song of the Night   *9'*

Elgar
Pomp and Circumstance March No. 4   *5'*

interval

new collaborative work
The Rough Guide to the
Proms Family Orchestra*   *c10'*
world premiere

Saint-Saëns
Introduction and Rondo capriccioso   *9'*

Britten
The Young Person's Guide to the Orchestra   *18'*

Jennifer Pike *violin*

BBC Proms Family Orchestra*
Lincoln Abbotts *director**

BBC Philharmonic
Tecwyn Evans *conductor*

A free family concert specially devised to give new and younger audiences a first taste of classical music and a flavour of the music to be heard throughout the season. There's the young Stravinsky arranging a Chopin waltz for ballerinas, and short pieces by Elgar and Holst, two of the three great British composers who died 75 years ago. There's 19-year-old violinist Jennifer Pike, one of the current crop of Radio 3's New Generation Artists, in a rarity by Holst and a showpiece by Saint-Saëns. And there's still no better introduction to the instruments of the orchestra than Britten's wonderful set of variations on a tune by Purcell, whose 350th anniversary we're celebrating this year. Plus there's a newly devised work, based on Britten's piece, designed for the BBC Proms Family Orchestra (which gives its debut performance at a Proms concert), and a new set of orchestral variations by Sir Richard Rodney Bennett based on a famous Irish tune first published by Purcell. *See 'Composers of the Year', pages 28–33; 'England at the Crossroads', pages 36–38; 'Bright Young Things', pages 48–51; 'New Music', pages 54–60*

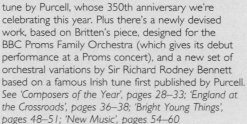

Jennifer Pike

Tecwyn Evans

Broadcast
RADIO Live on Radio 3
ONLINE Live and 'listen again' options at bbc.co.uk/proms

WEEKEND PROMMING PASS (SEE PAGE 148)

SUNDAY 26 JULY

Proms Plus
2.00pm, Royal Geographical Society **Film** BBC Two's *The Birth of British Music*, Parts 3 & 4: Haydn & Mendelssohn (120', awaiting classification). Introduced by the director, Francesca Kemp.
5.15pm, Royal College of Music **Proms Literary Festival** Sir Christopher Frayling, Rector of the Royal College of Art, and novelist D. J. Taylor join Rana Mitter to discuss the key cultural events of 1934, the year in which Delius, Elgar and Holst died.
Edited broadcast on Radio 3 during tonight's interval

7.00pm–c9.10pm

Holst
First Choral Symphony   *48'*

interval

Delius
Brigg Fair   *16'*

Elgar
Enigma Variations   *32'*

Susan Gritton *soprano*

BBC National Chorus of Wales
BBC Symphony Chorus
BBC National Orchestra of Wales
David Atherton *conductor*

Susan Gritton

Concluding our weekend marking the 75th anniversaries of the deaths of Delius, Elgar and Holst, David Atherton conducts the first Proms performance of Holst's ecstatic choral setting of poems by Keats. Delius's *Brigg Fair* took an old Lincolnshire folk song and distilled it into the very essence of nostalgia for England's idyllic rural past, while Elgar took the very essence of friendship and poured it into a dazzlingly inventive set of variations whose 1899 premiere transformed him overnight into England's foremost composer and turned 'Nimrod' into practically an alternative national anthem. Susan Gritton returns later this season as the seductive Dalila in Handel's *Samson* (Prom 47). *See 'England at the Crossroads', pages 36–38*

Broadcast
RADIO Live on Radio 3
ONLINE Live and 'listen again' options at bbc.co.uk/proms

MONDAY 27 JULY

1.00pm–c2.00pm

Proms Chamber Music at Cadogan Hall

Bizet
Chanson d'avril *3'*

Franck
Nocturne *4'*

Chabrier
Les cigales *4'*

Bachelet
Chère nuit *5'*

Duparc
Au pays où se fait la guerre *5'*

Ravel
Histoires naturelles – Le paon *5'*

Caplet
Le corbeau et le renard *4'*

Roussel
Réponse d'une épouse sage *3'*

Debussy
Fêtes galantes – Colloque sentimental *4'*

Honegger
Trois chansons de la petite sirène *3'*

Rosenthal
Chansons du monsieur Bleu – La souris d'Angleterre *3'*

Poulenc
La dame de Monte-Carlo *7'*

Susan Graham *mezzo-soprano*
Malcolm Martineau *piano*

Broadcast
RADIO Live on Radio 3
ONLINE Live and 'listen again' options at bbc.co.uk/proms

The sinuous and seductive world of French song is a speciality of the superlative American mezzo-soprano Susan Graham (see also Prom 19) and her duo partner Malcolm Martineau, who likens the delights on offer to a *menu gourmand*. And indeed there is a wide variety of musical dishes here, scanning a century of *mélodies françaises* and taking in the themes of night and nature, love and childhood, and culminating in Poulenc's bittersweet melodrama of defiance and regret.

There will be no interval

PCM 2
Spotlight on ... Susan Graham

'French music is a cornerstone of my career,' says Susan Graham. 'I got my breakthrough when I was still studying, performing in an obscure Massenet opera. The intense study of the language and style gave me a foundation for the rest of my career.'

Given her love of French music, it's no wonder Graham and pianist Malcolm Martineau have chosen an all-French programme. 'We wanted to devote a concert to French song, and show that there are so many different types of French vocal music, so we cover 100 years – from the mid-19th century to the mid-20th century, running the gamut of lush Romantic to more abstract music.

'There are sounds in French that don't exist in English,' the American mezzo-soprano explains, 'but I've had really good coaches that have instilled in me a discipline for making the proper sounds. Underneath all the subtlety and inflections, though, the French language still lives on in my own imagination as deeply exotic!

'Malcolm and I have such a great time on the platform. If you have a really close collaboration, you can throw your partner musical curve-balls and see if they can pick them up – like playing tennis.'

MONDAY 27 JULY

7.30pm–c9.35pm

Smetana
The Bartered Bride – Overture *6'*

Bartók
Dance Suite *17'*

Martinů
Concerto for two pianos *24'*

interval

Stravinsky
Petrushka (1947 version) *34'*

Jaroslava Pěchočová

**Jaroslava Pěchočová,
Václav Mácha** *pianos*

**BBC Symphony Orchestra
Jiří Bělohlávek** *conductor*

Václav Mácha

We open our survey of Stravinsky's ballets with the colourful tale of the puppet Petrushka, whose tragedy is played out at St Petersburg's Shrovetide fair (Stravinsky's earlier ballet for Diaghilev, *The Firebird*, can be heard tomorrow). Smetana's rustic Bohemian comedy *The Bartered Bride* – whose high-spirited overture makes a perfect curtain-raiser – is also set at a Slavic fair, while Bartók's *Dance Suite* draws in folk dances from Hungary, Romania and as far afield as Africa. Martinů's Concerto for two pianos, composed just after his First Symphony in 1943, betrays some of the tensions of two years earlier – when Martinů, like Bartók, was forced to flee to the USA – but ultimately finds release in an outpouring of the composer's characteristically effervescent vitality. See 'Master of the Dance', pages 16–25; 'A Frenzy of Fingerwork', pages 64–65

Broadcast
RADIO Live on Radio 3
ONLINE Live and 'listen again' options at bbc.co.uk/proms

TUESDAY 28 JULY

Proms Plus 5.15pm, Royal College of Music
Proms Intro Christopher Cook presents the first of three talks celebrating Stravinsky ballets, discussing *The Firebird* and *Petrushka* with Artistic Director of The Place, choreographer Richard Alston, and Stephanie Jordan, Research Professor at Roehampton University.
Edited broadcast on Radio 3 during tonight's interval

7.00pm–c9.25pm

John Casken
Orion over Farne   *21'*

Tchaikovsky
Piano Concerto No. 2 in G major   *40'*

interval

Stravinsky
The Firebird   *46'*

Stephen Hough *piano*

City of Birmingham Symphony Orchestra
Andris Nelsons *conductor*

Andris Nelsons

Andris Nelsons, the CBSO's new Music Director, makes his Proms debut. We celebrate both the International Year of Astronomy and John Casken's 60th birthday with the Barnsley-born composer's Basil Bunting-inspired evocation of Orion the hunter ever journeying towards the unknown across the Northumbrian night sky. Stephen Hough continues his traversal of the complete Tchaikovsky piano concertos with the unfairly neglected Concerto No. 2, whose middle movement unexpectedly flowers into a mini triple concerto for piano, violin and cello. We continue our survey of the complete Stravinsky ballets with the magical fairy-tale score he wrote for his first commission from Diaghilev's Ballets Russes.
See 'Master of the Dance', pages 16–25; 'Passions Ignited at the Piano', pages 42–45

Broadcast
RADIO Live on Radio 3
ONLINE Live and 'listen again' options at bbc.co.uk/proms

TUESDAY 28 JULY

10.15pm–c11.30pm

J. S. Bach
Komm, Jesu, Komm!, BWV 229   *10'*
Fürchte dich nicht, BWV 228   *10'*
Jesu, meine Freude, BWV 227   *22'*
Singet dem Herrn ein neues Lied, BWV 225   *18'*

Monteverdi Choir
English Baroque Soloists
Sir John Eliot Gardiner *conductor*

Even while Bach's great Passions languished unheard for almost a century after his death (until revived by Mendelssohn), his motets continued to be sung by the Leipzig choirs for which they were written. Few modern performers know Bach's music as intimately as Sir John Eliot Gardiner and his hand-picked choir and ensemble. They famously surveyed all 200-plus church cantatas during their millennial Bach Cantata Pilgrimage and now return to the Proms, following their acclaimed *St John Passion* at last year's Proms Bach Day, for a late-night selection of motets, including *Singet dem Herrn ein neues Lied* ('Sing to the Lord a new song'), a work which had even Mozart exclaiming, 'Now, there's a piece one can learn from.'

There will be no interval

Monteverdi Choir

SAME-DAY SAVER
Book for both Proms 16 and 17 and save (see page 148)

PROM 17
Spotlight on ... Sir John Eliot Gardiner

There may be only six surviving motets by Bach but, as Sir John Eliot Gardiner says, 'they form the peak of his art as a composer of choral music. They are of extraordinary compression and complexity, and make colossal demands on the singers for the exceptional virtuosity and stamina they require. Above all, there's the sense of abrupt changes of mood and texture, as well as of Bach's extraordinary sensitivity to the significance of each word.'

Gardiner's association with these works goes back to when he sang them as a child: by the age of 12 he had learnt them all by heart. 'They've stayed with me throughout my life,' he says. 'They're an endless pursuit.'

Gardiner points to the contrast of chorale hymn tunes and brilliant counterpoint in these motets, and the dramatic spatial effects created across the double choir in *Singet dem Herrn*. But most of all, says Gardiner, the motets 'can touch the listener as well as the performer, and they hold up a mirror to Bach, his essentially compassionate nature, the dance-like joy he takes in the praise of God, and his certitude in the nature of death.'

Broadcast
RADIO Live on Radio 3
ONLINE Live and 'listen again' options at bbc.co.uk/proms

WEEKEND PROMMING PASS (SEE PAGE 148)

WEDNESDAY 29 JULY

Proms Plus 5.45pm, Royal College of Music
Proms Composer Portrait Jörg Widmann discusses his new work in conversation with Tom Service, and introduces performances of some of his chamber works, as well as performing his own Fantasie for solo clarinet.
Edited broadcast on Radio 3 following this evening's Prom

7.30pm–c9.45pm

Jörg Widmann
Con brio   *12'*
UK premiere

Mozart
Violin Concerto No. 3 in G major, K216   *24'*

interval

Bruckner
Symphony No. 3 in D minor   *58'*

Arabella Steinbacher *violin*

Bamberg Symphony Orchestra
Jonathan Nott *conductor*

The Bamberg Symphony Orchestra made its Proms debut in 2006 and now reappears under its British-born Principal Conductor Jonathan Nott, who returns later this season to conduct the Gustav Mahler Jugendorchester (Prom 65). In a wide-ranging Austro-German programme, Bruckner's 'Wagner' Symphony – dedicated to the man he revered as 'the Master' – is prefaced by a Beethoven-inspired orchestral showpiece by rising young German composer Jörg Widmann and by the third of Mozart's five violin concertos, in which the multi-award-winning young German violinist Arabella Steinbacher makes her eagerly awaited Proms debut. See 'New Music', pages 54–60

Arabella Steinbacher

THURSDAY 30 JULY

Proms Plus 5.45pm, Royal College of Music
Proms Intro Louise Fryer talks to Professor John Deathridge and Mendelssohn's great-great-great-great-niece, Sheila Hayman, about the composer's music and life.

7.30pm–c9.50pm

Berlioz
Benvenuto Cellini – Overture   *12'*

La mort de Cléopâtre*   *22'*

interval

Mendelssohn
Symphony No. 2 in B flat major, 'Lobgesang'   *62'*

Susan Graham *mezzo-soprano**
Sally Matthews *soprano*
Sarah Castle *mezzo-soprano*
Peter Auty *tenor*

Hallé Choir
Hallé Youth Choir
Hallé
Sir Mark Elder *conductor*

Sir Mark Elder and the Hallé launch our bicentenary cycle of Mendelssohn's orchestral symphonies with the grand 'symphony-cantata' he wrote for the 400th anniversary of Gutenberg's invention of movable type; Sally Matthews, a star graduate of Radio 3's New Generation Artists scheme, leads the vocal forces in its extended choral 'Hymn of Praise'. Francophile Susan Graham returns, following her Proms Chamber Music recital (PCM 2), to sing the dying Queen of Egypt in Berlioz's dramatic cantata. It is prefaced by the dazzling overture the composer wrote for his opera about the artistic and amorous escapades of the great Renaissance sculptor Benvenuto Cellini. See 'Composers of the Year', pages 28–33; 'Bright Young Things', pages 48–51

Sir Mark Elder

FRIDAY 31 JULY

Proms Plus 5.45pm, Royal College of Music
Proms Literary Festival Victorian Season: Matthew Sweet introduces dramatic readings, celebrating the infamous villains from Victorian fiction, joined by award-winning biographer Michael Holroyd and writer Elaine Showalter.
Edited broadcast on Radio 3 during tonight's interval

7.30pm–c9.45pm

Stravinsky
Pulcinella   *40'*

interval

Schumann
Piano Concerto in A minor   *30'*

Mendelssohn
Symphony No. 5 in D major, 'Reformation'   *28'*

Nicholas Angelich *piano*
Karen Cargill *mezzo-soprano*
Andrew Staples *tenor*
Brindley Sherratt *bass*

Scottish Chamber Orchestra
Yannick Nézet-Séguin *conductor*

We continue our Stravinsky ballet series with the zany Neapolitan comedy in which the composer's reworkings of rediscovered 18th-century scores (reputedly by Pergolesi) resulted in the creation of a whole new – and wholly modern – neo-Classical style. And we continue our bicentenary survey of Mendelssohn's symphonies with the one that quotes Luther's great Reformation hymn 'Ein' feste Burg ist unser Gott'. The young French-Canadian maestro Yannick Nézet-Séguin (Gergiev's successor at the Rotterdam Philharmonic and now Principal Guest Conductor of the London Philharmonic Orchestra) makes his Proms debut, as does the prize-winning American pianist Nicholas Angelich in Schumann's popular concerto. See 'Master of the Dance', pages 16–25; 'Composers of the Year', pages 28–33

SATURDAY 1 AUGUST

Proms Plus

2.00pm, Royal College of Music **Proms Family Orchestra**
Dinosaurs and Dodos! The Proms Family Orchestra inspired by Darwin. See pages 72–79 for details of how to sign up.
4.45pm, Natural History Museum **Proms Family Orchestra** in performance

11.00am–c1.00pm

EVOLUTION! A Darwin-inspired extravaganza for kids

Barney Harwood *presenter*
Gemma Hunt *presenter*
with special guest **Sir David Attenborough**

BBC Concert Orchestra
Charles Hazlewood *conductor*

Sir David Attenborough

CBBC presenters Barney Harwood and Gemma Hunt unleash a natural selection of creatures in this child-friendly Prom inspired by the 200th anniversary of Charles Darwin's birth. Conductor Charles Hazlewood leads us from prehistoric Earth to outer space in John Williams's soundtracks to *Jurassic Park* and *Star Wars* – and we uncover the bird kingdom (with Delius's *On Hearing the First Cuckoo in Spring*) and insect life (in Arvo Pärt's *If Bach Had Been a Beekeeper*). Britten's 'Storm' interlude from his opera *Peter Grimes* represents the primal elements before the arrival of animals, while Copland's *Fanfare for the Common Man* anticipates the collective human spirit. Plus, there's a new beginning, as DJ and drum-and-bass producer Goldie (runner-up of last year's BBC Two *Maestro* competition) reveals a specially written, Darwin-inspired work – his first ever for a classical orchestra.

There will be one interval

Broadcast
TV Part recorded for future broadcast on BBC Two

SATURDAY 1 AUGUST

Proms Plus

2.00pm, Royal Geographical Society **Film** *Singin' in the Rain* (70', cert. U). The classic 1952 musical, starring Gene Kelly and Debbie Reynolds. Introduced by Matthew Sweet.
5.45pm, Royal College of Music **Proms Intro** Petroc Trelawny is joined by Patrick O'Connor and guests to explore the world of MGM film musicals.
Edited version broadcast on Radio 3 during tonight's interval

7.30pm–c9.30pm

A Celebration of Classic MGM Film Musicals

Kim Criswell *vocalist*
Sarah Fox *soprano*
Sir Thomas Allen *baritone*
Curtis Stigers *vocalist*

Maida Vale Singers
John Wilson Orchestra
John Wilson *conductor*

John Wilson

John Wilson and his hand-picked Orchestra celebrate 75 years of MGM musicals with songs from unforgettable movie classics, including *The Wizard of Oz*, *Meet Me in St Louis*, *Seven Brides for Seven Brothers*, *High Society*, *Gigi* and *Singin' in the Rain*. Amazingly, although all the original orchestral parts were lost when the studio destroyed its music library to make way for a car park, Wilson has succeeded in reconstructing the scores by painstakingly transcribing each soundtrack by ear. He is joined by starry singers from the classical and musical theatre worlds, as well as by the elite Maida Vale Singers.

There will be one interval

PROM 22

Spotlight on ... MGM film musicals

Even while he was studying classical scores at London's Royal College of Music, Gateshead-born John Wilson was drawn to the film scores of Hollywood's Golden Age. From the 1930s to the 1950s, says Wilson, 'the music was written by people like Max Steiner (godson of Richard Strauss) and Korngold in a late-Romantic idiom. There was a glamorous opulence, first-rate tunes clothed by the top orchestrators of the day.'

But the scores for many of these films were destroyed by MGM in 1969 and ended up as landfill for a golf course. 'The attitude of the time,' explains Wilson, 'was that they'd served their purpose. Nobody realised that this music might later be seen as great popular art of the 20th century.' Himself a prolific arranger, Wilson has taken up the challenge of reconstructing these lost scores, and has to date revived more than 130 routines from films including *The Wizard of Oz*, *Singin' in the Rain*, *The Band Wagon* and *High Society*.

Wilson brings his own orchestra to the Proms, which, he says, combines a 'virtuoso string section with a period-flavoured dance band'. As the song says, 'That's entertainment!'

The Wizard of Oz (1939)

Broadcast
RADIO Live on Radio 3
ONLINE Live and 'listen again' options at bbc.co.uk/proms
TV Live on BBC Two

SUNDAY 2 AUGUST

Proms Plus
2.00pm, Royal College of Music **Proms Family Orchestra** Dinosaurs and Dodos! The Proms Family Orchestra inspired by Darwin. See pages 72–79 for details of how to sign up.
4.45pm, Natural History Museum **Proms Family Orchestra** in performance

11.00am–c1.00pm

EVOLUTION! A Darwin-inspired extravaganza for kids

Barney Harwood presenter
Gemma Hunt presenter
with special guest **Sir David Attenborough**

BBC Concert Orchestra
Charles Hazlewood conductor

There will be one interval

For details, see Prom 21

Barney Harwood

Gemma Hunt

Charles Hazlewood

Broadcast
RADIO Live on Radio 3
ONLINE Live and 'listen again' options at bbc.co.uk/proms

WEEKEND PROMMING PASS • BEAT THE QUEUES AND SAVE MONEY (SEE PAGE 148)

SUNDAY 2 AUGUST

Proms Plus 5.45pm, Royal College of Music
Prom Literary Festival Victorian Season: Andrew Motion (Poet Laureate, 1999–2009) introduces his choice of Tennyson poems, 200 years after the great poet's birth. With readings performed by Fiona Shaw.
Edited version broadcast on Radio 3 during tonight's interval

7.30pm–c9.45pm

Ben Foskett
new work c12'
BBC commission: world premiere

Beethoven
Symphony No. 4 in B flat major   34'

interval

Berlioz
Te Deum 50'

Simon Preston organ

The Bach Choir
BBC Symphony Chorus
Crouch End Festival Chorus
Choristers of St Paul's Cathedral
Trinity Boys Choir
BBC Symphony Orchestra
Susanna Mälkki conductor

After conducting the Philharmonia Orchestra at last year's Proms, Susanna Mälkki returns for Berlioz's thunderous *Te Deum*. One of his most gargantuan as well as dramatic works, it involved almost 1,000 performers at its 1855 Paris premiere. Simon Preston returns after his solo recital in last year's Proms Bach Day to play the vital organ part, alongside massed choirs of adults and children. A new work by the young Paris-based British composer Ben Foskett prefaces the symphony in which, after the great leap forward of the 'Eroica' (Prom 25), Berlioz's idol, Beethoven, took a last look back at the more serene Classical style of Haydn. Tomorrow evening's Prom brings another Beethoven/Berlioz pairing.
See 'New Music', pages 54–60

PROM 24
Spotlight on ... Susanna Mälkki

Susanna Mälkki had a chance to prove her mettle last season when she filled in for Peter Eötvös at short notice, conducting the UK premiere of Eötvös's *Seven* with the BBC Symphony Orchestra. 'You need an adventurous attitude and a cool head to take on such situations,' says Mälkki. 'Fortunately,' she continues, 'Eötvös, being a conductor himself, writes out his scores very clearly and intelligently.'

Beethoven's Fourth Symphony is, according to Mälkki, 'a true pearl, though it is perhaps more "human"-sized, after the huge dimensions of his preceding "Eroica" symphony.' This, and a new work by Ben Foskett, are complemented by Berlioz's monumental *Te Deum*, which 'expresses universal divinity, rather than a particular religious impulse – there's a strong link to Beethoven in this respect,' Mälkki says. 'And, to express something larger than life, only a spectacular instrumentation – with large orchestra, the forces of several choruses, organ and soloist – could be enough for Berlioz. I cannot imagine any better venue than the Royal Albert Hall for this piece! Having the opportunity to conduct this at the Proms is a great privilege.'

Broadcast
RADIO Live on Radio 3
ONLINE Live and 'listen again' options at bbc.co.uk/proms

MONDAY 3 AUGUST

1.00pm–c2.00pm

Proms Chamber Music at Cadogan Hall

Haydn
String Quartet in F sharp minor, Op. 50 No. 4 *19'*

Britten
String Quartet No. 2 *31'*

Belcea Quartet

One of the UK's leading string quartets – and former Radio 3 New Generation Artists – pairs two strikingly original works in homage to two anniversary composers. Haydn's quartet comes from a period in the 1780s when he declared he was writing 'in a new and special way', and the second-movement set of variations is characteristically unexpected and quirky in its shifting contrasts of mood. Britten's atmospheric and evocative Second Quartet was composed in 1945 to celebrate the 250th anniversary of the death of Henry Purcell, and the finale is a 'Chacony' – an extended set of variations – which offers an extraordinary glimpse of Purcell's sound-world refracted through the imagination of a composer who loved his music. See 'Composers of the Year', pages 28–33; 'Bright Young Things', pages 48–51

There will be no interval

Belcea Quartet

Broadcast
RADIO Live on Radio 3
ONLINE Live and 'listen again' options at bbc.co.uk/proms

MONDAY 3 AUGUST

Proms Plus 5.15pm, Royal College of Music
Proms Composer Portrait Michael Jarrell, in conversation with Tom Service, discusses his new Proms co-commission and introduces performances of some of his chamber works.
Edited broadcast on Radio 3 following this evening's Prom

7.00pm–c10.05pm

Berlioz
Overture 'Les francs-juges' *12'*

Michael Jarrell
Sillages *c25'*
Orchestre de la Suisse Romande/BBC commission: world premiere of expanded version

interval

Berlioz
Symphonie funèbre et triomphale *34'*

interval

Beethoven
Symphony No. 3 in E flat major, 'Eroica' *50'*

Emmanuel Pahud *flute*
François Leleux *oboe*
Paul Meyer *clarinet*

BBC National Orchestra of Wales
Thierry Fischer *conductor*

The hero of the 'Eroica' was at first Napoleon but ultimately became Beethoven himself, triumphing over the adversity of his deafness. Berlioz's extraordinary *Symphonie* also contains a funeral march and an apotheosis but, unlike the 'Eroica', it was designed to accompany a real funeral cortège for the heroes of the 1830 July Revolution; the 'funeral oration' itself was delivered as a sonorous trombone solo salvaged from Berlioz's abandoned opera *Les francs-juges*. The title of Michael Jarrell's new piece refers to a wake of a different kind – the trace a ship leaves in the water; it was written with tonight's three soloists in mind, and is conducted by the Swiss composer's compatriot, Thierry Fischer. See 'New Music', pages 54–60

PROM 25
Spotlight on ... Thierry Fischer

Thierry Fischer, Principal Conductor of the BBC National Orchestra of Wales, is clearly excited about unleashing massive forces in the Royal Albert Hall for Berlioz's *Symphonie funèbre et triomphale*. 'This was one of the "dream pieces" I wanted to do in this space,' says an enthused Fischer. 'We will perform the original version without chorus and strings, and we'll have around 80 wind, brass and percussion players.

'It's at the same time a very noble and extravagant piece – you need a special occasion and the right space in which to create the depth of wind sound. Composed to mark the 10th anniversary of the 1830 French Revolution, this symphony was originally imagined to be played outdoors.

'It's sometimes extremely loud, with one or two sudden *pianissimos* that are quite radical, almost like a quick-edit in a movie. One of the challenges will be to save the players' energy; we'll have to pace ourselves in the last rehearsal, so we can preserve ourselves for the evening.

'I'm really looking forward to performing this extraordinary piece in the ideal space of the Royal Albert Hall.'

Broadcast
RADIO Live on Radio 3
ONLINE Live and 'listen again' options at bbc.co.uk/proms

TUESDAY 4 AUGUST

Proms Plus 4.45pm, Royal College of Music
Proms Literary Festival Victorian Season: Roy Hattersley and Professor Valentine Cunningham speak out in defence of the Victorian novel. Matthew Sweet chairs.
Edited version broadcast on Radio 3 during tonight's interval

6.30pm–c8.55pm

Mendelssohn
Symphony No. 1 in C minor   *32'*

Violin Concerto in E minor, Op. 64   *28'*

interval

Heinz Holliger
(S)irató   *15'*
UK premiere

Prokofiev
Romeo and Juliet – excerpts   *c25'*

Isabelle Faust violin

BBC National Orchestra of Wales
Thierry Fischer conductor

In the second of his two Proms with the BBC National Orchestra of Wales, Swiss-born Thierry Fischer introduces a new work by another of his compatriots: celebrating his 70th birthday this year, oboist-composer Heinz Holliger's punningly entitled *(S)irató* is an 'angry' lament for his teacher, the Hungarian composer Sándor Veress. We continue our Mendelssohn bicentenary celebrations with a pairing of his rarely heard First Symphony (completed when he was only 15, and later dedicated to the Philharmonic Society of London) and his ever-popular Violin Concerto, played by Isabelle Faust in her Proms debut. To end, a selection from Prokofiev's richly romantic Shakespearean ballet, *Romeo and Juliet*. See 'Composers of the Year', pages 28–33; 'New Music', pages 54–60

SAME-DAY SAVER Book for both Proms 26 and 27 and save (see page 148)

TUESDAY 4 AUGUST

10.00pm–c11.15pm

Sir Harrison Birtwistle
Carmen arcadiae mechanicae perpetuum   *10'*

Silbury Air   *16'*

Verses for Ensembles   *28'*

London Sinfonietta
David Atherton conductor

Sir Harrison Birtwistle

To celebrate Sir Harrison Birtwistle's 75th birthday the London Sinfonietta is rejoined by its founder-conductor David Atherton to perform three of the composer's major early works – all of which the ensemble premiered during its first decade. A virtuosic showpiece for brass, wind and percussion, the 1969 *Verses for Ensembles* was Birtwistle's earliest Sinfonietta score, and echoes the violent lyricism of his opera *Punch and Judy*. The other two works were both composed after Birtwistle had completed the first two acts of his massive 'lyric tragedy' *The Mask of Orpheus* (Prom 39). *Silbury Air*, named after the mysterious man-made mound in Wiltshire, uses a 'pulse labyrinth' to direct explorations of its 'imaginary landscapes', while in *Carmen arcadiae mechanicae perpetuum*, written for the Sinfonietta's 10th anniversary in 1978, six musical mechanisms are set in perpetual motion and then put on a collision course. See 'England at the Crossroads', pages 36–38

There will be no interval

Spotlight on … David Atherton

'My first experience of working with Harry [Birtwistle] was when I was asked to conduct the world premiere of his amazing opera *Punch and Judy* in 1968. The effect of this work was devastatingly overwhelming and the whole experience unforgettable. Having co-founded the London Sinfonietta the same year, I immediately commissioned Harry to write a work for the Sinfonietta's second season – the result: one of his finest instrumental works, *Verses for Ensembles*, a work that amply demonstrates the virtuosity of both composer and performers. Today it is as fresh as the day it was written.

'In the early years, performers were somewhat daunted by the extreme demands made by Harry. His sound-world was, and continues to be, so individual and uncompromisingly direct, and the technical requirements so demanding, that few orchestras and ensembles were able to perform his works with sufficient accuracy and dedication. The Sinfonietta played a huge role in making his earlier instrumental pieces accessible to wider audiences. To this day, one of the most gratifying aspects of working with the Sinfonietta is that the players and administration have lost none of the energy and enthusiasm that informed those early years. I am still constantly amazed at the rising standards and work ethics, as well as by the new directions into which the Sinfonietta continues to expand.

WEDNESDAY 5 AUGUST

Proms Plus 5.45pm, Royal College of Music
Proms Literary Festival Writer and film-maker Dennis Marks and Professor of Modern German Literature Karen Leeder explore the literary legacy of *fin-de-siècle* Vienna – the world that surrounded Gustav Mahler. Presented by Susan Hitch.
Edited version broadcast on Radio 3 during tonight's interval

7.30pm–c10.10pm

Stravinsky
Scènes de ballet   *15'*

Mozart
Bassoon Concerto in B flat major, K191   *18'*

interval

Mahler
Symphony No. 6 in A minor   *85'*

Karen Geoghegan *bassoon*

BBC Philharmonic
Gianandrea Noseda *conductor*

Gianandrea Noseda

In the first of their two Proms together, the BBC Philharmonic and its Chief Conductor Gianandrea Noseda are joined by the brilliant young Scottish bassoonist Karen Geoghegan, who was a popular runner-up in BBC Two's *Classical Star* in 2007 and here makes her Proms debut in Mozart's most unjustly neglected concerto. We continue our survey of the complete Stravinsky ballets with the 'featherweight and sugared' score he agreed to write for a 1944 Broadway revue (for a fee of $5,000 for 15 minutes, he boasted) and finished on the day of the liberation of Paris. And the concert ends with Mahler's powerfully, and perhaps prophetically, tragic Sixth Symphony, a record of one man's heroic struggle against the repeated hammer-blows of fate. See *'Master of the Dance'*, pages 16–25

Broadcast
RADIO Live on Radio 3
ONLINE Live and 'listen again' options at bbc.co.uk/proms

THURSDAY 6 AUGUST

Proms Plus 5.45pm, Royal College of Music
Proms Intro Conductor Gianandrea Noseda and General Manager of the BBC Philharmonic, Richard Wigley, join Martin Handley to introduce tonight's programme.
Edited version broadcast on Radio 3 during tonight's interval

7.30pm–c10.00pm

Mendelssohn
Symphony No. 4 in A major, 'Italian'   *30'*

Rossini
La donna del lago – 'Mura felice'   *10'*

La Cenerentola – 'Nacqui' all'affanno e al pianto … Non più mesta'   *7'*

interval

Sir Peter Maxwell Davies
Roma amor   *37'*

Respighi
Pines of Rome   *23'*

Vivica Genaux *mezzo-soprano*

Brass players from the Royal Northern College of Music
BBC Philharmonic
Gianandrea Noseda *conductor*

The BBC Philharmonic's Italian-born Chief Conductor Gianandrea Noseda pays tribute to his native land – and continues our cycle of Mendelssohn symphonies – with the sun-drenched work that the 21-year-old Mendelssohn composed while holidaying in Rome. Inspired by his own student days in Rome, Sir Peter Maxwell Davies's palindromically entitled *Roma amor* is a serenade to the city. Our cycle of Respighi's Roman trilogy opens with his vivid tableaux celebrating the capital's famous pines. Rossini's operatic retelling of the Cinderella story was his third stage-work for Rome's Teatro Valle. See *'Composers of the Year'*, pages 28–33; *'England at the Crossroads'*, pages 36–38

Broadcast
RADIO Live on Radio 3
ONLINE Live and 'listen again' options at bbc.co.uk/proms
TV Live on BBC Four

WEEKEND PROMMING PASS (SEE PAGE 148)

FRIDAY 7 AUGUST

Proms Plus 5.45pm, Royal College of Music
Proms Intro Young Composers' Winners Day
Members of the Aurora Orchestra perform commissions by 2008 winners of the BBC Proms Inspire Young Composers' Competition.
Edited highlights broadcast by Radio 3 following the Prom on 19 August

7.30pm–c9.35pm

Respighi
Fountains of Rome   *18'*

Helen Grime
Virga   *5'*

Stravinsky
Jeu de cartes   *23'*

interval

Oliver Knussen
Cleveland Pictures   *c23'*
UK premiere

Balakirev, orch. Casella
Islamey   *9'*

BBC Symphony Orchestra
Oliver Knussen *conductor*

Oliver Knussen

Oliver Knussen, the BBC SO's new Artist-in-Association, introduces his latest piece, due to be premiered by The Cleveland Orchestra in May. He also gives the first Proms performance of Helen Grime's dramatic evocation of the electric atmosphere before a storm. Stravinsky's 1936 ballet *Jeu de cartes* is a musical poker game in three 'deals', ending with the Joker trounced by a royal flush. In the second part of his Roman trilogy, Respighi takes us on a dawn-to-dusk tour of the city's most famous fountains; while, in orchestrating Balakirev's 'oriental fantasy', Casella propelled an already virtuosic keyboard piece into even more exotic extremes. See *'Master of the Dance'*, pages 16–25; *'Composers of the Year'*, pages 28–33; *'New Music'*, pages 54–60

Broadcast
RADIO Live on Radio 3
ONLINE Live and 'listen again' options at bbc.co.uk/proms
TV Live on BBC Four

SATURDAY 8 AUGUST

7.00pm–c9.00pm

Tchaikovsky
Piano Concerto No. 1 in B flat minor   *35'*

interval

Lutosławski
Concerto for Orchestra   *29'*

Respighi
Roman Festivals   *25'*

Stephen Hough piano

National Youth Orchestra of Great Britain
Vasily Petrenko conductor

The National Youth Orchestra of Great Britain returns under its new Principal Conductor, Vasily Petrenko, who made his Proms debut with the Royal Liverpool Philharmonic Orchestra last year. In his traversal of the Tchaikovsky piano concertos, Liverpool-born Stephen Hough reaches that great warhorse the Concerto No. 1. With its brilliant textures and hints of Polish folk music, Lutosławski's 1954 concerto is a real showpiece for any orchestra, while our final instalment of Respighi's Roman trilogy brings the first performance at the Proms of *Roman Festivals* – a cinematic survey of the Eternal City's ever-changing festivals, from ancient gladiatorial combats in the Circus Maximus to the *Petrushka*-esque carnival bustle in the Piazza Navona. See 'Passions Ignited at the Piano', pages 42–45

Broadcast
RADIO Live on Radio 3
ONLINE Live and 'listen again' options at bbc.co.uk/proms
TV Live on BBC Two (with Maestro Cam via red button)

SUNDAY 9 AUGUST • MULTIPLE PIANOS DAY

3.00pm–c5.15pm

FAURÉ, orch. Rabaud
Dolly (suite)   *17'*

Mozart
Concerto for two pianos in E flat major, K365   *25'*

interval

Anna Meredith
new work   *c10'*
BBC commission: world premiere

Lutosławski
Variations on a Theme of Paganini   *6'*

Saint-Saëns
The Carnival of the Animals   *23'*

Ludovic Morlot

Katia and Marielle Labèque pianos
Philip Moore and
Simon Crawford-Phillips pianos
Lydia and Sanya Biziak pianos

Britten Sinfonia
Ludovic Morlot conductor

We open our day of music for two or more pianos with Fauré's delightful *Dolly* suite, originally written for two players at one keyboard. Mozart's double concerto is full of playful intimacy, while Saint-Saëns's playful zoological suite contrasts with Lutosławski's virtuosic reworking of a famous Paganini Caprice. There's also a new work for two pianos by Anna Meredith, whose nation-hopping *froms* introduced her to Proms audiences last year. See 'New Music', pages 54–60; 'A Frenzy of Fingerwork', pages 64–65

SAME-DAY SAVER
Book for both Proms 32 and 33 and save (see page 148)

Broadcast
RADIO Live on Radio 3
ONLINE Live and 'listen again' options at bbc.co.uk/proms

7.30pm–c10.00pm

Antheil
Ballet mécanique   *16'*

John Adams
Grand Pianola Music   *30'*

interval

Edward Gardner

Bartók
Sonata for two pianos and percussion*   *26'*

Stravinsky
Les noces (sung in Russian)   *24'*

Tatiana Monogarova soprano
Elena Manistina mezzo-soprano
Vsevolod Grivnov tenor
Kostas Smoriginas bass

John Constable, Rolf Hind,
François-Frédéric Guy, Ashley Wass,
Llŷr Williams pianos
Philip Moore and
Simon Crawford-Phillips pianos*
Colin Currie, Sam Walton percussion*

BBC Singers
London Sinfonietta
Edward Gardner conductor

A 20th-century view of multiple pianos, featuring up to eight hands in a programme including George Antheil's notorious *Ballet mécanique*, the 'wild party' of John Adams's *Grand Pianola Music* and a continuation of our Stravinsky ballets series. See 'Master of the Dance', pages 16–25; 'Bright Young Things', pages 48–51; 'A Frenzy of Fingerwork', pages 64–65;

Broadcast
RADIO Live on Radio 3
ONLINE Live and 'listen again' options at bbc.co.uk/proms

MONDAY 10 AUGUST

1.00pm–c2.00pm

Proms Chamber Music at Cadogan Hall

Purcell
Chacony *7'*

Mozart
Divertimento in F major, K138 *12'*

John Woolrich
Capriccio *c20'*
world premiere

Stravinsky
Concerto in D major *13'*

Scottish Ensemble
Jonathan Morton *violin/director*

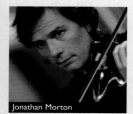
Jonathan Morton

A rich variety of string music spanning three centuries. At this programme's heart is a new piece by John Woolrich, framed by classic works by Mozart and by Purcell, whose imaginative use of form in his Chacony was such an inspiration for Britten's String Quartet No. 2 (Prom PCM 3). Stravinsky's mercurial Concerto of 1946 casts an ironic eye back to the musical past as it extracts every ounce of colour and contrast from the strings. With its disjointed motor rhythms, the music twists and turns in the air like some crazy dance, alternately gawky and elegant, high-spirited and nostalgic – the perfect vehicle to demonstrate the versatility and vitality of this exciting ensemble of players. See *'Composers of the Year', pages 28–33; 'New Music', pages 54–60*

There will be no interval

Broadcast
RADIO Live on Radio 3
ONLINE Live and 'listen again' options at bbc.co.uk/proms

MONDAY 10 AUGUST

Proms Plus 5.45pm, Royal College of Music
Family Music Intro Bring your family to hear the incredible stories behind tonight's music. Bring your instrument and join in with members of the Bournemouth Symphony Orchestra.

7.30pm–c9.50pm

Stravinsky
The Fairy's Kiss *44'*

interval

Tchaikovsky
Violin Concerto *35'*

Khachaturian
Spartacus – excerpts *c20'*

Gayane – Hopak *3'*

Julian Rachlin *violin*

Bournemouth Symphony Orchestra
Kirill Karabits *conductor*

Kirill Karabits

Fast-rising young Ukrainian maestro Kirill Karabits makes his Proms debut as the Bournemouth Symphony Orchestra's new Principal Conductor. The brilliant Lithuanian-born violinist Julian Rachlin returns to the Proms to play the tenderly lyrical, extrovertly virtuosic concerto by Tchaikovsky, to whose music and memory Stravinsky paid tribute in his Hans Christian Andersen-inspired ballet, *The Fairy's Kiss*. By contrast, Khachaturian's colourful Soviet-era ballet *Spartacus* celebrates the Thracian gladiator whose rebel slave army almost defeated the might of Rome. See *'Master of the Dance', pages 16–25*

Broadcast
RADIO Live on Radio 3
ONLINE Live and 'listen again' options at bbc.co.uk/proms

TUESDAY 11 AUGUST

Proms Plus 5.45pm, Royal College of Music
Proms Literary Festival Victorian Season: Ian McMillan explores the power of the partnership between Gilbert and Sullivan, with writer Ian Bradley, author of a complete annotated version of their works.
Edited version broadcast on Radio 3 during tonight's interval

7.30pm–c10.10pm

Sullivan
Patience *115'*
(semi-staged)

Rebecca Bottone *Patience*
Felicity Palmer *Lady Jane*
Pamela Helen Stephen *Lady Angela*
Elena Xanthoudakis *Lady Ella*
Sophie-Louise Dann *Lady Saphir*
Simon Butteriss *Reginald Bunthorne*
Toby Stafford-Allen *Archibald Grosvenor*
Donald Maxwell *Colonel Calverley*
Graeme Danby *Major Murgatroyd*
Bonaventura Bottone *Lt. The Duke of Dunstable*

Chorus of English National Opera
BBC Concert Orchestra
Sir Charles Mackerras *conductor*
Martin Duncan *director*

Rebecca Bottone

Following his earlier appearance this season conducting the music of Delius, Elgar and Holst (Prom 12), Sir Charles Mackerras returns as one of our greatest living exponents of G&S and, in the wake of conducting *HMS Pinafore* in 2005, he now presides over a specially created semi-staging of the 1881 operetta in which Gilbert took a swipe at the then fashionable Aesthetic movement and its artistic figurehead, Oscar Wilde.

There will be one interval

Broadcast
RADIO Live on Radio 3
ONLINE Live and 'listen again' options at bbc.co.uk/proms

WEDNESDAY 12 AUGUST

Proms Plus 5.15pm, Royal College of Music
Proms Literary Festival Journalist Matthew Parris and Professor Lynda Mugglestone join Ian McMillan to celebrate the life and literary legacy of Handel's great contemporary Samuel Johnson, 300 years after his birth.
Edited version broadcast on Radio 3 during tonight's interval

7.00pm–c9.20pm

Handel

Solomon – The Arrival of the Queen of Sheba   *3'*

Coronation anthem 'Let thy hand be strengthened'   *9'*

Semele – excerpts   *22'*

Coronation anthem 'My heart is inditing'   *12'*

interval

Coronation anthem 'The King shall rejoice'   *9'*

Motet 'Salve Regina'   *12'*

Organ Concerto in F major, Op. 4 No. 4 (original version)   *16'*

Coronation anthem 'Zadok the Priest'   *6'*

Carolyn Sampson soprano
Alastair Ross organ

The Sixteen
Harry Christophers conductor

To celebrate Handel's 250th anniversary, Harry Christophers and The Sixteen intersperse the four glorious anthems that Handel wrote for George II's coronation with other Handelian hits, including excerpts from his satirical semi-opera *Semele*, and the well-known *Arrival of the Queen of Sheba* from *Solomon*. See 'Composers of the Year', pages 28–33

Broadcast
RADIO Live on Radio 3
ONLINE Live and 'listen again' options at bbc.co.uk/proms
TV Recorded for broadcast on BBC Two on 15 August at 8.45pm

WEDNESDAY 12 AUGUST

10.15pm–c11.20pm

Philip Glass

Violin Concerto   *23'*

Symphony No. 7, 'A Toltec Symphony'   *36'*
UK premiere

Gidon Kremer violin

BBC Symphony Chorus
BBC Scottish Symphony Orchestra
Dennis Russell Davies conductor

Philip Glass

Gidon Kremer

One of the most prolific, influential and instantly identifiable composers of our age, Philip Glass made an impact on the course of 20th-century music with his pioneering 'Minimalist' scores, going on to write major film scores – from *Koyaanisqatsi* and *Kundun* to *The Truman Show* and *The Hours* – and innumerable dance, theatre and operatic works. In the first Prom ever devoted exclusively to Philip Glass's music, his first major orchestral score, the 1987 Violin Concerto, is played by Gidon Kremer, who made the premiere recording, and conducted by Dennis Russell Davies, a long-term champion of Glass's music. Premiered in 2004, the 'Toltec Symphony' takes its title from the ancient pre-Columbian culture that reigned in Mesoamerica long before the coming of the Europeans, though vestiges of it still survive among the indigenous peoples of Mexico today. See 'New Music', pages 54–60

There will be no interval

PROM 37
Spotlight on ... Dennis Russell Davies

Philip Glass's Violin Concerto – of which conductor Dennis Russell Davies is a co-dedicatee – is one of the composer's most popular works. 'It is both popular and a demanding addition to the modern violin literature,' Davies explains. 'It's a big attraction for concert-goers who aren't normally drawn to new music, and also to people who are more interested in the visual arts or science.'

The 'Toltec Symphony', which receives its UK premiere tonight, has its roots in the ancient civilisation of central America. 'Philip visits this area every year to climb in the mountains,' Davies says. 'In the second movement, the chorus sings syllables which have no translation. Philip recorded a local old man singing and wrote down the syllables as he understood them. When he asked other locals what they meant, they didn't know, though they recognised the sounds.'

Davies believes Glass will be among the enduring American composers. 'As with Cage and Copland, Glass may not have created a particular "school" of music, but he has found with his music a way to reach across to non-traditional audiences.'

Broadcast
RADIO Live on Radio 3
ONLINE Live and 'listen again' options at bbc.co.uk/proms

WEEKEND PROMMING PASS • BEAT THE QUEUES AND SAVE MONEY (SEE PAGE 148)

THURSDAY 13 AUGUST

Proms Plus 6.15pm, Royal College of Music
Proms Intro In the second of three talks celebrating Stravinsky's ballets, Christopher Cook discusses *The Rite of Spring* with Director of the Royal Ballet, Monica Mason, and choreographer Millicent Hodgson, who has reconstructed Nijinsky's original choreography for *The Rite of Spring*.
Edited version broadcast on Radio 3 during tonight's interval

8.00pm–c9.55pm

Ravel
La valse *12'*

Unsuk Chin
Cello Concerto *c30'*
BBC commission: world premiere

interval

Stravinsky
The Rite of Spring *33'*

Alban Gerhardt *cello*

BBC Scottish Symphony Orchestra
Ilan Volkov *conductor*

Ilan Volkov

The BBC Scottish SO, under Chief Conductor Ilan Volkov, pair two Diaghilev commissions. With its pounding rhythms, cataclysmic upheavals and savage scenario of a young girl dancing herself to death, Stravinsky's *The Rite of Spring* is still genuinely earth-shattering – no wonder Nijinsky's 1913 production provoked a riot. Begun as a homage to the Viennese waltz but twisted by his wartime experiences into a darker vision of a society whirling to disaster, Ravel's *La valse* was actually rejected by Diaghilev and only finally staged in the year of his death, choreographed by Nijinsky's sister Bronislava. Unsuk Chin's new Cello Concerto was written specially for Alban Gerhardt, an early member of Radio 3's New Generation Artists scheme. See 'Master of the Dance', pages 16–25; 'Bright Young Things', pages 48–51; 'New Music', pages 54–60

Broadcast
RADIO Live on Radio 3
ONLINE Live and 'listen again' options at bbc.co.uk/proms
TV Live on BBC Four (with Maestro Cam via red button)

FRIDAY 14 AUGUST

Proms Plus 5.45pm, Royal College of Music
Proms Inspire Day The Aurora Orchestra performs the winning entries of this year's BBC Proms Inspire Young Composers' Competition. *(Limited capacity)*
Edited version broadcast by Radio 3 following the Prom on 19 August

7.30pm–c9.55pm

Jonny Greenwood
Popcorn Superhet Receiver *18'*

Stravinsky
Apollo *30'*

interval

Sir Harrison Birtwistle
The Mask of Orpheus – The Arches* *58'*

Cast to include:
Alan Oke *Orpheus (the man)*
Christine Rice *Euridice (the woman)*
Anna Stéphany *Euridice (the myth)/Persephone*
Claron McFadden *Hecate*

BBC Singers
BBC Symphony Orchestra
Martyn Brabbins *conductor*
Ryan Wigglesworth *2nd conductor**
Ian Dearden *sound projection*

A decade in the making, Birtwistle's 'lyric tragedy' was the culmination of a long-standing obsession with the Orpheus myth. To mark the composer's 75th birthday, the BBC SO presents its central act – in which Orpheus journeys to the Underworld through a series of 17 arches – contrasting its dazzling complexity with the classical poise of Stravinsky's ballet *Apollo*. The opener by Radiohead's Jonny Greenwood won the Radio 3 Listeners' Award at the 2006 British Composer Awards. See 'Master of the Dance', pages 16–25; 'England at the Crossroads', pages 36–38; 'Bright Young Things', pages 48–51

Broadcast
RADIO Live on Radio 3
ONLINE Live and 'listen again' options at bbc.co.uk/proms
TV Live on BBC Four

SATURDAY 15 AUGUST

Proms Plus
2.00pm, Royal Geographical Society **Film** *Stravinsky: Once, at a Border…* (166', exempt from classification). Tony Palmer's profile of the composer, featuring contributions from family, colleagues and friends. Introduced by the director.
5.45pm **Proms Literary Festival** Philip Pullman, author of the award-winning trilogy *His Dark Materials*, talks to Susan Hitch about the powerful myth of Orpheus.
Edited version broadcast on Radio 3 during tonight's interval

7.30pm–c9.40pm

Stravinsky
Orpheus *32'*

interval

Beethoven
Symphony No. 9 in D minor, 'Choral' *65'*

Rebecca Evans *soprano*
Caitlin Hulcup *mezzo-soprano*
Anthony Dean Griffey *tenor*
James Rutherford *bass-baritone*

City of Birmingham Symphony Chorus
BBC Scottish Symphony Orchestra
Ilan Volkov *conductor*

Rebecca Evans

In his last Proms appearance as the BBC Scottish SO's Chief Conductor, Ilan Volkov conducts the annual Proms performance of Beethoven's ever-inspiring hymn to universal brotherhood. We continue our survey of the complete Stravinsky ballets with his austerely beautiful, almost abstract, ritualisation of the music-driven Orpheus myth that has obsessed European composers from before Monteverdi to Birtwistle (Prom 39) and beyond. See 'Master of the Dance', pages 16–25; 'Bright Young Things', pages 48–51

Broadcast
RADIO Live on Radio 3
ONLINE Live and 'listen again' options at bbc.co.uk/proms
TV Recorded for broadcast on BBC Four on 11 September at 7.30pm

Simon Butterworth (Volkov); Sian Trenberth (Evans)

SUNDAY 16 AUGUST • INDIAN VOICES DAY

10.30am–c1.30pm

Indian Voices 1 – Khyal and Kerala

Pandit Ram Narayan *sarangi*

Manjiri Asnare Kelkar *khyal singer*

Pandits Rajan and Sajan Mishra *khyal singers*

Asima

with
Aruna Narayan *sarangi*
Akbar Latif *tabla*
Babar Latif *tabla*
Sudhir Nayak *harmonium*

Pandits Rajan and Sajan Mishra

Our Proms Indian Voices day begins with a concert of north Indian classical *khyal* singing, featuring Pandit Ram Narayan, the greatest living sarangi (short-necked fiddle) player; Manjiri Asnare Kelkar, the rising star of the Jaipur–Gwalior *khyal* school; the two Mishra brothers, the foremost exponents of the virtuoso Varanasi vocal style; and Asima, an iconoclastic, boundary-breaking young vocal ensemble from Kerala. See 'Indian Voices', pages 68–69

There will be one interval

Broadcast
RADIO Live on Radio 3
ONLINE Live and 'listen again' options at bbc.co.uk/proms

Proms Plus Kensington Gardens (except 5.45pm)
2.00pm–6.00pm Indian Voices in the Park Free performances of folk music and dance from Rajasthan (including *ghoomer* dance) and Gujarat (including *ras* and *garba* dances). Also featuring the vocal fusion ensemble Asima, and incorporating:
Proms Family Orchestra and Chorus (2.00pm) Participate in the Proms Bollywood Family Orchestra and Chorus and learn how to dance Bollywood style! See pages 72–79 for more details.
5.45pm Proms Literary Festival (Royal College of Music)
Prize-winning author Jamila Gavin and 'Binglish' theatre director Jatinder Verma join Rana Mitter to explore great Bollywood stories.
Edited version broadcast on Radio 3 during tonight's interval

7.30pm–c10.00pm

Indian Voices 2 – Bollywood

Shaan *vocalist*

The Groove

Honey's Dance Academy

Following the afternoon of free music-making and dance at Indian Voices in the Park, Kensington Gardens, our Proms Indian Voices celebration culminates in an all-singing, all-dancing Bollywood extravaganza fronted by the popular Indian TV talent show host and award-winning singer Shaan and his band, plus the Bollywood moves of Honey's Dance Academy. See 'Indian Voices', pages 68–69

There will be one interval

Shaan

SAME-DAY SAVER Book for both Proms 41 and 42 and save (see page 148)

Honey's Dance Academy

Manjiri Asnare Kelkar

PROM 41
Spotlight on ... *khyal* singing

Central to present-day north-Indian classical music, the *khyal* form is fundamentally vocal but spreads through the gamut of instrumental genres. It is the art of elaborating on a raga – the modal, scale-like essence of both melody and mood – and later on a *tala*, or rhythmic cycle. *Khyal* grew from the old song form of *dhrupad*, itself rooted in Persian and indigenous music, as a more virtuosic vehicle for performers.

There's a subtle balance between improvisation and memorised composition. The free opening, or *alap*, can be a brief prelude or a patient, eventually thrilling ascent to a top note. Next, a pulse develops and the pace increases in stages. If a percussionist is involved, one or more pieces will follow using a *tala*, often with a rousing conclusion.

One fascination is the way style varies from one hereditary school of performance to another. With the Mishra brothers from the Varanasi school and Manjiri Asnare Kelkar from Jaipur, the morning Prom on Indian Voices day brings a rare chance to compare two of the *khyal*'s most renowned exponents.

In association with the Asian Music Circuit

Broadcast
RADIO Live on Radio 3
ONLINE Live and 'listen again' options at bbc.co.uk/proms

PCM 5

PROM 43

Seats
£7 to £35

PRICE
BAND **A**

MONDAY 17 AUGUST

1.00pm–c2.00pm

Proms Chamber Music at Cadogan Hall

Mendelssohn
Prelude and Fugue in E minor, Op. 35 No. 1   *9'*

J. S. Bach, transcr. Busoni
Chorale Preludes 'Wachet auf, ruft uns die Stimme'; 'Nun freut euch, lieben Christen g'mein'; 'Ich ruf' zu dir, Herr Jesu Christ'   *12'*

Brahms
Variations and Fugue on a Theme by Handel   *28'*

Llŷr Williams *piano*

Llŷr Williams

A recital of 'Baroque Reflections' devised by this remarkably accomplished former Radio 3 New Generation Artist and inspired by Brahms's magnificent homage to the music of anniversary composer Handel. Busoni and Mendelssohn reinvented Bach for their own times: Busoni by transcribing for the piano a selection of organ pieces, and Mendelssohn by breathing vivid new life into an archaic form in a turbulent Prelude and Fugue. Brahms worked on an even broader canvas with the music of Handel, transforming a theme from one of his keyboard suites and building to a glorious climax. Handel, that supreme man of the theatre, would have loved it! *See 'Composers of the Year', pages 28–33; 'Bright Young Things', pages 48–51*

There will be no interval

Broadcast
RADIO Live on Radio 3
ONLINE Live and 'listen again' options at bbc.co.uk/proms

MONDAY 17 AUGUST

Proms Plus 5.45pm, Royal College of Music
Proms Composer Portrait Louis Andriessen, in conversation with Andrew McGregor, discusses *The Hague Hacking* and introduces performances of some of his chamber works.
Edited broadcast on Radio 3 following this evening's Prom

7.30pm–c9.30pm

Falla
El amor brujo – three dances   *10'*

Louis Andriessen
The Hague Hacking   *18'*
UK premiere

interval

Ravel
Mother Goose (ballet)   *28'*

Boléro   *15'*

Katia and Marielle Labèque *pianos*

Philharmonia Orchestra
Esa-Pekka Salonen *conductor*

Esa-Pekka Salonen

Esa-Pekka Salonen makes his first Proms appearance as the Philharmonia's new Principal Conductor. The Labèque sisters return for their third and final appearance this season (see Proms 1 & 32), to celebrate the 70th birthday of the radical Dutch composer Louis Andriessen with the UK premiere of his new concerto – partly inspired by a *Tom and Jerry* cartoon, partly by a hardcore brand of house music – which they and Salonen premiered in Los Angeles in January. (Andriessen's 1970s classic *De staat* is performed in Prom 58.) Dance drives the rest of the programme, from Falla's fiery flamenco vision of a midnight exorcism to Ravel's magical fairy-tale evocations and the relentless crescendo of his *Boléro*. *See 'New Music', pages 54–60; 'A Frenzy of Fingerwork', pages 64–65*

PROM 43
Spotlight on … Katia and Marielle Labèque

The Labèque sisters Katia and Marielle are making multiple appearances during this season's mini-festival of Multiple Pianos, with tonight's Prom being their third and last. 'We love everything about the Proms,' says Katia, 'the ambience, the audience, the Hall. It's such a joy to be back.'

Following Poulenc's tongue-in-cheek two-piano concerto (Prom 1) and works by Mozart and Lutosławski (Prom 32), the piece the Labèque sisters perform tonight is the most recent, and the most radical of the four.

'In order to play with freedom in the performance [the world premiere in Los Angeles in January this year], we had to spend a lot of time with the score,' says Katia. 'We blocked off two months completely without any concerts. Louis was great, because he sent us the piece well in advance.'

As well as augmenting the orchestral palette with intrusions from an electric guitar, bass guitar and cimbalom, Andriessen employs the device of 'hocketing'. Here, as Katia explains, 'each of us plays consecutive notes in the musical phrase, alternating one after the other – which is pure madness, because if you miss a note you are completely lost!'

Broadcast
RADIO Live on Radio 3
ONLINE Live and 'listen again' options at bbc.co.uk/proms

TUESDAY 18 AUGUST

Proms Plus 5.15pm, Royal College of Music
Proms Intro Join Iván Fischer and members of the Budapest Festival Orchestra for a special family concert designed to introduce classical music to 5- to 12-year-olds in an entertaining and interactive environment.

7.00pm–c9.10pm

Prokofiev
Overture on Hebrew Themes *8'*

Bartók
Violin Concerto No. 2 *36'*

interval

Dvořák
Symphony No. 7 in D minor *40'*

Leonidas Kavakos *violin*

Budapest Festival Orchestra
Iván Fischer *conductor*

Iván Fischer

Hungary's leading orchestra returns to the Proms, this time with Leonidas Kavakos, the soloist in Bartók's Second Violin Concerto, which combines breathtaking virtuosity with passionate lyricism. Prokofiev wrote his klezmer-tinged overture in New York in 1919 for a group of Jewish refugees who had all been fellow-students of his in St Petersburg; his 1934 arrangement, for a Haydn-sized band, was made two years before his return to the USSR. Dvořák's most darkly dramatic and passionate symphony, commissioned by the Philharmonic Society of London and premiered under its auspices in 1885, has remained especially popular with UK audiences ever since.

TUESDAY 18 AUGUST

10.00pm–c11.15pm

Ukulele Orchestra of Great Britain

The all-singing, all-strumming players of the Ukulele Orchestra of Great Britain have devised a special programme for their first Proms appearance, to include a rendition of that Last Night favourite, Parry's *Jerusalem*, as you've never heard it before. All music is fair game in this unique ensemble's book of 'depraved musicology', typically resulting in a collision of punk, rock 'n' roll and toe-tapping oldies. Other classics receiving the UOGB treatment in tonight's Prom are Wagner's *The Ride of the Valkyries*, Eric Coates's march *The Dambusters*, an excerpt from Beethoven's Ninth Symphony (yes, really!) — and unorthodox arrangements of songs by The Who and the Sex Pistols. You may never hear music in quite the same way again!

SAME-DAY SAVER
Book for both Proms 44 and 45 and save (see page 148)

There will be no interval

PROM 45
Spotlight on ...

Ukulele Orchestra of Great Britain

When the grandly titled Ukulele Orchestra of Great Britain began — with a one-off gig in a London pub in 1985 — none of its members could have imagined that they would land a slot at the Proms.

Playing a wide variety of music, from punk to pop and country to classical, this quirky miniature orchestra believes that all good music will also sound good on a 'uke'. 'We use ukuleles of different registers — high ones, low ones, ones in the middle — rather like a string ensemble,' explains George Hinchliffe, the ensemble's co-founder. 'We use different techniques — playing with fingers, plectrums and slides. Different instruments have different characters — mellow or bright — and we add vocals and even whistling. We've sometimes been urged to incorporate other instruments — like percussion — but that would obscure the character of the ukulele.'

And Hinchliffe highlights a glorious ancestry for the ukulele, arguing that early plucked string instruments, and Renaissance guitar-like instruments — much smaller than modern ones — also had four strings and were tuned in the same way as a 'uke'.

WEDNESDAY 19 AUGUST

Proms Plus 5.45pm, Royal College of Music
Proms Intro Andrew McGregor discusses the music of Shostakovich with musicologist David Nice and lecturer in Russian Dr Philip Ross Bullock (University of Oxford).
Edited version broadcast on Radio 3 during tonight's interval

7.30pm–c10.00pm

Detlev Glanert
Shoreless River   *c20'*
BBC co-commission with WDR Symphony Orchestra, Cologne, Royal Concertgebouw Orchestra, Amsterdam, and National Symphony Orchestra, Washington DC: UK premiere

Rachmaninov
Rhapsody on a Theme of Paganini   *25'*

interval

Shostakovich
Symphony No. 11, 'The Year 1905'   *63'*

Denis Matsuev *piano*

BBC Symphony Orchestra
Semyon Bychkov *conductor*

Semyon Bychkov

Renowned Shostakovich interpreter Semyon Bychkov conducts the composer's astonishingly powerful and strikingly cinematic 1957 symphony, which on the surface commemorates the failed anti-Tsarist uprising of 1905, but deep down rages at the Soviet authorities. Detlev Glanert's new piece is a foretaste of his forthcoming opera, *Das Holzschiff* ('The Wooden Ship'). Winner of the 1998 Moscow Tchaikovsky Competition, and recently acclaimed by *Gramophone* as 'a virtuoso in the grandest of Russian traditions', Denis Matsuev makes his Proms debut in Rachmaninov's devilishly demanding set of variations on Paganini's most famous Caprice.
See 'New Music', pages 54–60

PROM 46
Spotlight on … Denis Matsuev

'Stewed in Russian juices' is how *Gramophone* magazine described Denis Matsuev's recent recording, *Unknown Rachmaninov*, made at Rachmaninov's villa 'Senar' near Lake Lucerne, on a 1929 Steinway owned by the composer. Since winning the International Tchaikovsky Competition in 1998, Matsuev has been performing with a range of international conductors and orchestras and, though he has previously appeared in London, this year marks his debut at the Proms, for which he plays the popular *Rhapsody on a Theme of Paganini*.

'Rachmaninov is like an idol to me,' says Matsuev. 'In the last two years I've been playing and recording his music a lot around the world – including around 55 performances of the Third Concerto. As you can hear on his own recordings, his sound as a pianist, his energy, his phrasing were all something to marvel at.'

Matsuev shares his enthusiasm with Sir Henry Wood, founder-conductor of the Proms, who asked the great composer-pianist to appear at his Jubilee Concert in 1938, and declared him 'an inventive and original composer … in the first rank', whose piano concertos 'are valued … throughout the realm of music'.

THURSDAY 20 AUGUST

Proms Plus 4.45pm, Royal College of Music
Proms Intro Join tonight's conductor Harry Bicket and musicologist Dr Berta Joncas for an introduction to Handel's oratorio *Samson*, with Catherine Bott.
Edited version broadcast on Radio 3 during tonight's first interval

6.30pm–c10.20pm

Handel
Samson   *165'*

Mark Padmore

Susan Gritton *Dalila*
Iestyn Davies *Micah*
Mark Padmore *Samson*
Neal Davies *Manoa*
Christopher Purves *Harapha*
Lucy Crowe *Israelite Woman/Philistine Woman/Virgin*
Ben Johnson *Israelite Man/Philistine Man/Messenger*

The Choir of The English Concert
The New Company
The English Concert
Harry Bicket *conductor*

Based on Milton and composed within a month of *Messiah* (Prom 68), Handel's *Samson* opens with Israel's former champion blinded and imprisoned but ends in triumph as he topples the temple of Dagon down upon the feasting Philistines and, through his suicide, sets his people free. In the 250th anniversary of the composer's death, the hero's heart-breaking lament over his lost sight – 'Total eclipse! No sun, no moon, all dark amidst the blaze of noon!' – gains added poignancy from the knowledge that Handel himself would soon go blind. Baroque specialist Harry Bicket makes his Proms debut conducting a starry line-up of British singers, several making their second appearance this season. See 'Composers of the Year', pages 28–33

There will be two intervals

FRIDAY 21 AUGUST

Proms Plus 5.15pm, Royal College of Music
Proms Literary Festival Edward Stourton talks to Rana Mitter about how the literature of the Middle East has informed his understanding of the region – and selects his personal choice of readings.
Edited version broadcast on Radio 3 during the interval of Prom 50

7.00pm–c9.15pm

Liszt
Les préludes   17'

Wagner
Tristan und Isolde – Prelude and Liebestod   18'

interval

Berlioz
Symphonie fantastique   55'

West–Eastern Divan Orchestra
Daniel Barenboim conductor

It was in 1999 in Weimar that the Israeli pianist-conductor Daniel Barenboim and the Palestinian-American cultural historian, the late Edward Said, jointly founded the West–Eastern Divan Orchestra – a unique ensemble bringing together young players from both sides of the Arab–Israeli divide in what Barenboim insists is not 'an orchestra for peace' but 'an orchestra against ignorance', and which is now universally acclaimed as simply a superb orchestra, however you label it. To open our weekend celebrating the Divan's 10th anniversary, we return to its roots in Weimar, where, as the city's music director for over a decade, Liszt championed the works of both Wagner and Berlioz.

PROM 48
Spotlight on ... Daniel Barenboim

It's 10 years since Daniel Barenboim and Edward Said formed the West–Eastern Divan Orchestra, bringing together young Israeli and Arab musicians. A decade on, the orchestra continues to shine as a beacon of dialogue between nations in conflict.

'We have no political line,' says Barenboim. 'We don't tell people what to think – except that we are convinced there is no military solution to the conflict and that the futures of Palestine and Israel are inextricably linked.'

The range of the orchestra's four weekend events at the Proms attests to Barenboim's aim to expose the young players to as wide a range of repertoire as possible. 'The orchestra is also an education project: among our players we have three members of the Berlin Philharmonic – but we also have some less experienced players; we see to it that the more experienced ones help the others.'

Despite a decade of success, the fact remains, says Barenboim, 'that we cannot yet play in all of the Middle Eastern countries. The full dimension of our project will be realised only when we are able to play in all the countries represented by the members of the orchestra.'

Broadcast
RADIO Live on Radio 3
ONLINE Live and 'listen again' options at bbc.co.uk/proms
TV Broadcast at 7.30pm on BBC Four (with Maestro Cam via red button)

FRIDAY 21 AUGUST

10.15pm–c11.30pm

Mendelssohn
Octet   32'

Berg
Chamber Concerto   38'

Michael Barenboim violin
Karim Said piano

Members of the
West–Eastern Divan Orchestra
Daniel Barenboim conductor

Bicentenary composer Felix Mendelssohn was only 16 when he wrote his masterly Octet: sprinkled with the same fairy dust as his music for *A Midsummer's Night Dream* (Prom 72), the airy, scampering Scherzo is said to have been inspired by lines from Goethe, the great German poet whom he had met in Weimar at the age of 12 and whose Persian-inspired collection, *West–Eastern Divan*, gave tonight's orchestra its name. The 2009 recipient of the Moses Mendelssohn Medal – named after the composer's philosopher grandfather and awarded to campaigners for peace and tolerance – Daniel Barenboim conducts Berg's musical monument to friendship with an ensemble including his violinist son Michael and his pianist protégé Karim Said (a relative of the orchestra's co-founder, the late Edward Said). See 'Composers of the Year', pages 28–33

There will be no interval

SAME-DAY SAVER
Book for both Proms 48 and 49 and save (see page 148)

West–Eastern Divan Orchestra

Broadcast
RADIO Live on Radio 3
ONLINE Live and 'listen again' options at bbc.co.uk/proms

SATURDAY 22 AUGUST

Proms Plus

2.30pm, Royal College of Music **Proms Intro** Members of the West–Eastern Divan Orchestra perform Boulez's *Anthèmes II* and *Messagesquisse*. Daniel Barenboim conducts the latter work, and introduces the performances.
Recorded for future broadcast on Radio 3.

4.00pm, Royal Geographical Society **Film** *Knowledge is the Beginning* (114', exempt from classification). Paul Smaczny's profile of the West–Eastern Divan Orchestra. Introduced by Mariam Said.

7.30pm–c10.15pm

Beethoven

Fidelio *(concert performance; sung in German, with English narration written by Edward Said)*   120'

Waltraud Meier

Waltraud Meier *Leonore/narrator*
Simon O'Neill *Florestan*
Peter Mattei *Don Pizarro*
Sir John Tomlinson *Rocco*
Adriana Kučerová *Marzelline*
Stephan Rügamer *Jaquino*
Viktor Rud *Don Fernando*

BBC Singers
Geoffrey Mitchell Choir
West–Eastern Divan Orchestra
Daniel Barenboim *conductor*

Our celebration of the West–Eastern Divan Orchestra's 10th anniversary ends with Beethoven's only foray into the form, *Fidelio* is at once a passionate protest against political injustice and a paean to the power of human love. Conducted by Daniel Barenboim, it is sung in German by an international cast, using the English narration written by the orchestra's co-founder, the late Edward Said, in which the opera's heroine describes the events of the day in which she single-handedly rescued her husband from illegal incarceration and summary execution.

There will be one interval

Broadcast
RADIO Live on Radio 3
ONLINE Live and 'listen again' options at bbc.co.uk/proms
TV Broadcast at 8.10pm on BBC Two

SUNDAY 23 AUGUST

Proms Plus 4.45pm, Royal College of Music
Proms Literary Festival Broadcaster and chaplain Revd Richard Coles, and novelist Janice Galloway, talk to Susan Hitch about the diaries, poetry and letters of composers who also had a literary gift.
Edited version broadcast on Radio 3 during tonight's interval

6.30pm–c8.45pm

Haydn

Symphony No. 101 in D major, 'Clock'   28'

Szymanowski

Stabat mater *(sung in Polish)*   25'

interval

Brahms

Violin Concerto in D major   40'

Helena Juntunen *soprano*
Monica Groop *mezzo-soprano*
Scott Hendricks *baritone*
Joshua Bell *violin*

BBC Symphony Chorus
BBC Symphony Orchestra
Osmo Vänskä *conductor*

Osmo Vänskä makes a welcome return to the Proms to conduct the first Haydn symphony in this season's bicentenary celebration of the 'father' of the form: with its tick-tocking slow movement, the 'Clock' was one of the 12 'London' Symphonies that the Austrian composer wrote for his two extended visits to the capital in the early 1790s.

Osmo Vänskä

Szymanowski's tenderly devotional *Stabat mater* was partly inspired by the tragic death of a teenage niece. Co-star of the 2007 Last Night, Joshua Bell returns to play Brahms's Hungarian-accented Violin Concerto (returning again to make chamber music in Monday's PCM 6). See 'Composers of the Year', pages 28–33

PROM 51
Spotlight on ... Joshua Bell

Since his first appearance at the Proms nearly 20 years ago, Joshua Bell has returned with a wide range of repertoire – covering the central classics (in concertos by Beethoven, Bruch, Mendelssohn and Tchaikovsky), as well as more recent additions to the violin concerto canon by Barber, Bernstein and Nicholas Maw.

This year he brings Brahms's Violin Concerto – the work that Hans von Bülow famously quipped had been written *against* the violin, rather than for it – conducted by Osmo Vänskä, Music Director of the Minnesota Orchestra, with whom Bell recently toured Europe.

The day after his concerto performance, Bell returns in the more intimate setting of Cadogan Hall (see PCM 6, next page) for a recital featuring his long-standing chamber music partner Steven Isserlis, whom he counts as 'one of my biggest influences'. It was with Isserlis that Bell appeared at the Proms in 2000, playing Brahms's Double Concerto, but the two had first worked together nearly 15 years before that.

The packed diaries of both musicians mean they have to work hard to plan their rehearsals, but the partnership of these distinguished soloists invariably makes for thrilling musical results.

Broadcast
RADIO Live on Radio 3
ONLINE Live and 'listen again' options at bbc.co.uk/proms

PCM 6

PROM 52

Seats
£7 to £35

PRICE
BAND A

MONDAY 24 AUGUST

1.00pm–c2.00pm

Proms Chamber Music at Cadogan Hall

Schumann
Phantasiestücke, Op. 88   *19'*

Mendelssohn
Piano Trio No. 1 in D minor, Op. 49   *28'*

Joshua Bell *violin*
Steven Isserlis *cello*
Dénes Várjon *piano*

Two distinguished concerto soloists (see Proms 51 and 57) join forces with a brilliant young Hungarian pianist for music of poetry and drama. Schumann's four delightful character-pieces were his first works for piano trio, composed in 1842 when he was experiencing what his wife Clara called 'the joy of discovering a passion for trios'. Schumann himself dubbed Mendelssohn's Opus 49 'the master trio of our age'; it carries this anniversary composer's hallmarks of an expressive 'song without words' and a fleeting 'scherzo', encircled by the Romantic sweep and grandeur of its outer movements. *See 'Composers of the Year', pages 28–33*

There will be no interval

Steven Isserlis

Broadcast
RADIO Live on Radio 3
ONLINE Live and 'listen again' options at bbc.co.uk/proms

MONDAY 24 AUGUST

Proms Plus 5.45pm, Royal College of Music
Proms Intro Suzy Klein discusses Schnittke and Shostakovich with composer, writer and broadcaster Gerard McBurney and Russian music expert Dr Marina Frolova-Walker.
Edited version broadcast on Radio 3 during tonight's interval

7.30pm–c9.45pm

Schnittke
Nagasaki   *36'*
UK premiere

interval

Shostakovich
Symphony No. 8 in C minor   *60'*

Elena Zhidkova *mezzo-soprano*

London Symphony Chorus
London Symphony Orchestra
Valery Gergiev *conductor*

Valery Gergiev returns at the helm of the LSO to conduct the most devastatingly bleak of Shostakovich's three 'war symphonies'. Composed at the time of the Battle of Stalingrad, the Eighth is paired with the belated

Valery Gergiev

UK premiere of Schnittke's early, Orff-influenced oratorio, an agonised expression of solidarity with the victims of the second atomic bomb, dropped on the city of Nagasaki the day before Japan's surrender. Heavily criticised by the Soviet Composers' Union, it only received its 1959 broadcast premiere (on Moscow World Service Radio) after Shostakovich's recommendation, and was not publicly performed until 2006. *See 'New Music', pages 54–60*

PROM 52
Spotlight on … Elena Zhidkova

Russian mezzo-soprano Elena Zhidkova made her surprise London debut in January as a last-minute replacement for the scheduled Judith in an LSO concert performance of Bartók's *Duke Bluebeard's Castle*, conducted by the orchestra's Principal Conductor, Valery Gergiev, with whom she now makes her Proms debut. Although her career has been mainly based in Germany for the past decade, Gergiev has long been a formative influence: 'He was already the Opera Director of the Mariinsky Theatre in St Petersburg when I was studying at the Conservatory,' she says, 'and I regularly attended his performances. He began inviting interesting directors and singers, and introduced all sorts of innovations and modern productions – it was terribly exciting! He opened a door for us onto the international stage, making Russian works better known abroad and expanding the repertoire back at home to include even such pieces as Wagner's *Ring*.'

As for the two composers in this concert, she says: 'Shostakovich and Schnittke are united by a heartfelt humanist ideal, which doesn't just speak to the Russian people but can reach out to an English audience as well. I love the passion that is rooted in the Russian soul!'

Broadcast
RADIO Live on Radio 3
ONLINE Live and 'listen again' options at bbc.co.uk/proms

TUESDAY 25 AUGUST

Proms Plus 5.15pm, Royal College of Music
Proms Intro Sir Roger Norrington is joined by musicians from the Orchestra of the Age of Enlightenment to discuss the influences of anniversary composers Purcell, Handel, Haydn and Mendelssohn on British musical life. Presented by Sara Mohr-Pietsch.
Edited version broadcast on Radio 3 during tonight's interval

7.00pm–c9.15pm

Joyce DiDonato

Purcell
Abdelazar – suite 9'

Handel
Xerxes – 'Ombra mai fù' 4'

Alcina – 'Ah, mio cor!' 10'

Water Music – Suite No. 2 in D major 12'

Haydn
Scena di Berenice 13'

interval

Mendelssohn
Symphony No. 3 in A minor, 'Scottish' 38'

Joyce DiDonato mezzo-soprano

Orchestra of the Age of Enlightenment
Sir Roger Norrington conductor

The host of last year's Last Night, Sir Roger Norrington returns to conduct music by all four of this year's major anniversary composers. Purcell's music to *Abdelazar* gave Britten the theme he used, 250 years later, in his *Young Person's Guide to the Orchestra* (Prom 13), and American mezzo-soprano Joyce DiDonato performs two Handel arias as well as Haydn's 'mad scene' for the distraught Berenice, who begs the gods to let her join her lover in death. Mendelssohn's evocative 'Scottish' symphony was conceived on the same 1829 holiday as his *Hebrides* overture (Prom 70). See 'Composers of the Year', pages 28–33

TUESDAY 25 AUGUST

10.15pm–c11.30pm

Michael Nyman
The Draughtsman's Contract – selection 23'

The Musicologist Scores c20'
BBC commission: world premiere

Six Celan Songs – Blume; Psalm 10'

The Cook, The Thief, His Wife and Her Lover – Memorial 12'

Anu Komsi soprano

Michael Nyman Band
Michael Nyman director

Michael Nyman

Now best known for his soundtracks to such movies as *The Piano*, *Gattaca* and *Wonderland*, Michael Nyman started out as a musicologist, editing scores by Handel and Purcell; as a critic he coined the term 'Minimalism'; and as a composer he first made his name by putting the music of classical masters through the Minimalist mill to generate raunchy, rhythmically propulsive, raucously energetic new works, such as his score for Peter Greenaway's 1982 film *The Draughtsman's Contract* and the grief-frozen *Memorial* (which featured in Greenaway's later *The Cook, The Thief, His Wife and Her Lover*) – both of which are Purcell-based. Now, to celebrate the year's two big Baroque anniversaries the Michael Nyman Band makes its Proms debut with a new work echoing the Purcell and Handel pieces heard in Prom 53. See 'Composers of the Year', pages 28–33; 'New Music', pages 54–60

SAME-DAY SAVER
Book for both Proms 53 and 54 and save (see page 148)

There will be no interval

WEDNESDAY 26 AUGUST

Proms Plus 5.45pm, Royal College of Music
Proms Intro Anthony Sayer, a veteran cellist of the BBC Scottish Symphony Orchestra, and other guests, join Ian Skelly to discuss the thrills and challenges of playing in an orchestra.

7.30pm–c9.40pm

John Adams
Slonimsky's Earbox 13'

Mozart
Piano Concerto No. 20 in D minor, K466 32'

interval

R. Strauss
Symphonia domestica 45'

Shai Wosner piano

BBC Scottish Symphony Orchestra
Donald Runnicles conductor

Edinburgh-born Donald Runnicles returns with the BBC Scottish SO, of which he becomes Chief Conductor this autumn. Richard Strauss's outsize orchestral hymn to domestic harmony not only reveals the secrets of the marital bedroom but throws in both the baby and the bathwater too. Radio 3 New Generation Artist Shai Wosner – who made his Proms debut in 2003 playing Mozart's Concerto for three pianos with Saleem Abboud Ashkar (Prom 69) alongside Daniel Barenboim and the West–Eastern Divan Orchestra (Proms 48–50) – returns to make his solo debut in Mozart's turbulently clouded D minor Concerto. And John Adams's 1996 teaser pays tribute to the wit and wisdom of the Russian musical polymath Nicolas Slonimsky. See 'Bright Young Things', pages 48–51

THURSDAY 27 AUGUST

Proms Plus 5.45pm, Royal College of Music
Proms Literary Festival Stephen Venables, the first Briton to climb Everest without supplementary oxygen, and Chris Smith, former Secretary of State for Culture, Media and Sport and mountaineering enthusiast, talk to Ian McMillan about their favourite mountain writing.
Edited version broadcast on Radio 3 during tonight's interval

7.30pm–c10.15pm

Rebecca Saunders
traces c15'
UK premiere of revised version

Chopin
Piano Concerto No. 2 in F minor 46'

interval

R. Strauss
An Alpine Symphony 50'

Lang Lang piano

Staatskapelle Dresden
Fabio Luisi conductor

Following last night's depiction of domestic life in the Strauss household, we continue with his mountain-inspired final tone-poem, performed by the orchestra to which it was dedicated (and which premiered no fewer than nine of his 15 operas) under its current Chief Conductor, Fabio Luisi, here making his Proms debut. Ever a favourite with Proms audiences, Lang Lang returns to perform Chopin's brilliantly virtuosic, Romantically poetic and mazurka-capped F minor Concerto. And the evening opens with a revised, expanded version of a 2006 work by British-born, Berlin-based Rebecca Saunders. *See 'New Music', pages 54–60*

Lang Lang

FRIDAY 28 AUGUST

Proms Plus 5.15pm, Royal College of Music
Proms Intro In the last of three talks celebrating Stravinsky's ballets, Louise Fryer is joined by composer Julian Anderson and Stravinsky biographer Stephen Walsh to discuss Stravinsky's final ballet, *Agon*.
Edited version broadcast on Radio 3 during tonight's interval

7.00pm–c9.20pm

Stravinsky
Agon 24'

Tchaikovsky
Concert Fantasia in G major, Op. 56 29'

interval

Tchaikovsky
Variations on a Rococo Theme 18'

Francesca da Rimini 24'

Stephen Hough piano
Steven Isserlis cello

BBC Symphony Orchestra
David Robertson conductor

David Robertson

Our survey of Stravinsky's ballets ends with the dazzling set of 12 dances for 12 dancers that the septuagenarian composer based on material taken from a 17th-century dance manual but re-energised through his own unique 20th-century viewpoint. To conclude our series of Tchaikovsky's concertante works, Stephen Hough signs off his one-man piano marathon with the curiously neglected Concert Fantasia, while cellist Steven Isserlis returns (after making chamber music in Monday's PCM 6) to relish the 18th-century charms of the 'Rococo' Variations. And the BBC SO's Principal Guest Conductor, David Robertson, ends the concert with Tchaikovsky's Dantesque tale of forbidden love and eternal punishment. *See 'Master of the Dance', pages 16–25; 'Passions Ignited at the Piano', pages 42–45*

FRIDAY 28 AUGUST

10.15pm–c11.40pm

Louis Andriessen
De staat 35'

Steve Martland
Beat the Retreat 13'

Cornelis de Bondt
Doors Closed* 23'
London premiere

Netherlands Wind Ensemble
Lukas Vis conductor
Bart Schneemann 2nd conductor*

The Netherlands Wind Ensemble, 50 this year, marks the 70th birthday of radical Dutch Minimalist Louis Andriessen and the 50th of his leading British pupil Steve Martland with performances of Andriessen's classic polemic *De staat* and Martland's jazz-rock 'dance fantasia' *Beat the Retreat*, commissioned by the BBC for its 1995 Purcell tercentenary celebrations. Another former pupil of Andriessen, Cornelis de Bondt creates an idiosyncratic death ritual in *Doors Closed* out of a fusion between the funeral march from Beethoven's 'Eroica' (Prom 25) and Dido's Lament from Purcell's *Dido and Aeneas* (Prom 76). Two of tonight's works call for two or more pianos, in a nod to our Multiple Pianos celebration. *See 'New Music', pages 54–60; 'A Frenzy of Fingerwork', pages 64–65*

There will be no interval

SAME-DAY SAVER
Book for both Proms 57 and 58 and save (see page 148)

Steve Martland

Seats £12 to £54 | PRICE BAND C

SATURDAY 29 AUGUST • NEW GENERATION ARTISTS AT CADOGAN HALL

DAY TICKET • FOUR CONCERTS FOR THE PRICE OF THREE (SEE PAGE 151)

WEEKEND PROMMING PASS (SEE PAGE 148)

SATURDAY 29 AUGUST

PCM 7 — 11.00am–c12.10pm

Haydn
String Quartet in
G major, Op. 77
No. 1   *22'*

Alexander Goehr
Since Brass, nor
Stone …   *14'*

Beethoven
String Quartet in
C minor, Op. 18
No. 4   *33'*

Jerusalem Quartet
Pavel Haas Quartet
Colin Currie percussion

There will be no interval

*See 'Composers of the
Year', pages 28–33;
'Bright Young Things',
pages 48–51*

Pavel Haas Quartet

PCM 8 — 1.00pm–c2.00pm

J. S. Bach
Partita No. 3 in E major
for solo violin,
BWV 1006   *19'*

Bartók
Sonata for solo violin   *27'*

Alina Ibragimova violin
Tai Murray violin

There will be no interval

*See 'Bright Young Things',
pages 48–51*

Alina Ibragimova

Tai Murray

PCM 9 — 2.30pm–c3.35pm

Mozart
Piano Quartet in
E flat major, K493   *26'*

Spohr
Nonet   *31'*

Kungsbacka Trio
Lawrence Power viola
Aronowitz Ensemble
Galliard Ensemble
Luis Cabrera double bass

There will be no interval

*See 'Bright Young Things',
pages 48–51*

Lawrence Power

Kungsbacka Trio

PCM 10 — 4.30pm–c5.40pm

Delius
Cello Sonata   *13'*

Holst
Four Songs for tenor
and violin, Op. 35   *7'*

Six Songs for baritone
and piano, Op. 15 –
selection   *7'*

Elgar
Violin Sonata   *26'*

Natalie Clein cello
Andrew Kennedy tenor
Jonathan Lemalu
bass-baritone
Jennifer Pike violin
Tom Poster piano

There will be no interval

*See England at the
Crossroads', pages 36–38;
'Bright Young Things',
pages 48–51*

Natalie Clein

PROM 59

Proms Plus 5.15pm, Royal College of Music
Proms Intro Join Dr Elmar Weingarten, Executive Director of
the Tonhalle Orchestra Zurich, and musicians from the orchestra,
in conversation with Rob Cowan.

7.00pm–c9.00pm

Schubert
Rosamunde – Overture   *10'*

Schubert/Osvaldo Golijov
She Was Here   *14'*
UK premiere

interval

Mahler
Symphony No. 4 in G major   *60'*

Dawn Upshaw soprano

Tonhalle Orchestra Zurich
David Zinman conductor

Dawn Upshaw

We welcome back American
soprano Dawn Upshaw – who
memorably made a chart-topping
recording of Górecki's *Symphony
of Sorrowful Songs* with tonight's
conductor, David Zinman, in the
early 1990s – to sing Osvaldo
Golijov's acclaimed new work:
an intense exploration of loss and
consolation, in which the Argentine-born composer
draws upon a ravishing range of colours to enhance
the poetic imagery of four Schubert songs. Tonight's
opener represents the more public face of Schubert,
with the overture published as part of his incidental
music to Helmina von Chézy's play *Rosamunde*. Upshaw
returns after the interval to provide the angel's-eye view
of Heaven at the end of Mahler's Fourth Symphony.
See 'New Music', pages 54–60

Broadcast
RADIO Live on Radio 3
ONLINE Live and 'listen
again' options at
bbc.co.uk/proms

Broadcast
RADIO Live on Radio 3
ONLINE Live and 'listen
again' options at
bbc.co.uk/proms

Broadcast
RADIO Live on Radio 3
ONLINE Live and 'listen
again' options at
bbc.co.uk/proms

Broadcast
RADIO Live on Radio 3
ONLINE Live and 'listen
again' options at
bbc.co.uk/proms

Broadcast
RADIO Live on Radio 3
ONLINE Live and 'listen
again' options at bbc.co.uk/proms
TV Live on BBC Two

SUNDAY 30 AUGUST • NEW GENERATION ARTISTS AT CADOGAN HALL

DAY TICKET • FOUR CONCERTS FOR THE PRICE OF THREE (SEE PAGE 151)

WEEKEND PROMMING PASS (SEE PAGE 148)

SUNDAY 30 AUGUST

PCM 11

11.00am–c12.25pm

Haydn
String Quartet in D major, Op. 20 No. 4   18'

Debussy
String Quartet   25'

Szymanowski
String Quartet No. 1 in C major, Op. 37   18'

Bree
Allegro for four string quartets   11'

Meta4
Psophos Quartet
Royal String Quartet
Pavel Haas Quartet

There will be no interval

See 'Composers of the Year', pages 28–33; 'Bright Young Things', pages 48–51

Psophos Quartet

Broadcast
RADIO Live on Radio 3
ONLINE Live and 'listen again' options at bbc.co.uk/proms

PCM 12

1.00pm–c2.00pm

J. S. Bach
Suite No. 4 in E flat major for solo cello, BWV 1010 (transcr. for viola)   23'

Kodály
Sonata for solo cello   30'

Maxim Rysanov viola
Danjulo Ishizaka cello

There will be no interval

See 'Bright Young Things', pages 48–51

Maxim Rysanov

Broadcast
RADIO Live on Radio 3
ONLINE Live and 'listen again' options at bbc.co.uk/proms

PCM 13

2.30pm–c3.40pm

Schumann
Adagio and Allegro in A flat major, Op. 70   8'

Brahms
Two songs for alto, viola and piano   11'

Martinů
Promenades for flute, violin and harpsichord   10'

Mahler
Des Knaben Wunderhorn – selection   c25'

Antoine Tamestit viola
Christine Rice mezzo-soprano
Shai Wosner piano
Emily Beynon flute
Tai Murray violin
Mahan Esfahani harpsichord
Alice Coote mezzo-soprano
Steven Osborne piano

There will be no interval

See 'Bright Young Things', pages 48–51

Steven Osborne

Broadcast
RADIO Live on Radio 3
ONLINE Live and 'listen again' options at bbc.co.uk/proms

PCM 14

4.30pm–c5.40pm

Arias and duets by **Purcell** and **Handel** c20'

Haydn
Arias and Canzonets   10'

Mendelssohn
Piano Trio No. 2 in C minor, Op. 66   26'

Elizabeth Watts soprano
Daniela Lehner mezzo-soprano
Allan Clayton tenor
Alison Balsom trumpet
Mahan Esfahani harpsichord
Tai Murray violin
Andreas Brantelid cello
Shai Wosner piano

There will be no interval

See 'Composers of the Year', pages 28–33; 'Bright Young Things', pages 48–51

Elizabeth Watts

Broadcast
RADIO Live on Radio 3
ONLINE Live and 'listen again' options at bbc.co.uk/proms

PROM 60

Proms Plus 5.45pm, Royal College of Music
Family Music Intro An introduction for all the family to tonight's programme of French, Canadian and Russian music. Bring your instrument along and take part.

7.30pm–c9.35pm

Vivier
Orion   13'
UK premiere

Ravel
Piano Concerto in G major   22'

interval

Prokofiev
Piano Concerto No. 1 in D flat major   15'

Musorgsky, orch. Ravel
Pictures at an Exhibition   30'

Martha Argerich piano

Royal Philharmonic Orchestra
Charles Dutoit conductor

Martha Argerich

Iconic pianist Martha Argerich returns to the Proms to play both Ravel's jazzy G major Concerto (its blue-note harmonies coloured by the composer's visits to Harlem and Hollywood) and Prokofiev's one-movement Concerto No. 1 (the 21-year-old's precocious mix of wrong-note modernism, percussive rhythms and post-Romantic rhapsody). Musorgsky's musical memorial to a dead painter friend was known mainly in its original solo piano form before Ravel added the colours of his unrivalled orchestral imagination. In the International Year of Astronomy, Claude Vivier's intriguing exploration of the echoing vastnesses of outer space is brought to the UK by Charles Dutoit, who conducted its 1980 premiere in Montreal. See 'New Music', pages 54–60

Broadcast
RADIO Live on Radio 3
ONLINE Live and 'listen again' options at bbc.co.uk/proms

MONDAY 31 AUGUST • NEW GENERATION ARTISTS AT CADOGAN HALL
DAY TICKET • FOUR CONCERTS FOR THE PRICE OF THREE (SEE PAGE 151)

11.00am–c12.15pm

Chopin
Four Mazurkas,
Op. 24   *11'*

Mazurka in A minor,
Op. 17 No. 4   *5'*

Mendelssohn
Songs Without Words –
selection   *13'*

Stravinsky
The Rite of Spring
(two-piano version)   *33'*

Simon Trpčeski *piano*
Simon Crawford-Philips,
Ashley Wass *pianos*

There will be no interval

*See 'Master of the Dance',
pages 16–25; 'Composers
of the Year', pages 28–33;
'Bright Young Things',
pages 48–51*

Simon Trpčeski

1.00pm–c2.00pm

J. S. Bach
Sonata in E flat major
for flute and keyboard
BWV 1031   *10'*

Suite No. 2 in B minor,
BWV 1067 –
Badinerie   *2'*

John McCabe
Study No. 12
(Sonata)   *c12'*
*BBC commission:
world premiere*

J. S. Bach,
arr. Villa-Lobos
Preludes and
Fugues – selection
(arr. for eight cellos)   *10'*

Villa-Lobos
Bachiana Brasileira
No. 5   *9'*

Sharon Bezaly *flute*
Mahan Esfahani *harpsichord*
Ashley Wass *piano*
Ailish Tynan *soprano*
Claudio Bohórquez,
Andreas Brantelid,
Natalie Clein,
Danjulo Ishizaka,
Guy Johnston,
Li-Wei, Marie Macleod,
Christian Poltéra *cellos*

There will be no interval

*See 'Bright Young Things',
pages 48–51; 'New
Music', pages 54–60*

2.30pm–c3.45pm

Britten
Cello Suite No. 3   *21'*

Schubert
String Quintet in
C major, D956   *47'*

Christian Poltéra *cello*
Szymanowski Quartet
Claudio Bohórquez *cello*

There will be no interval

*See 'Bright Young Things',
pages 48–51*

Claudio Bohórquez

Christian Poltéra

4.30pm–c5.40pm

Stravinsky
The Soldier's Tale –
suite   *14'*

Tom Arthurs
And Distant Shore   *c10'*
*BBC co-commission with
the Royal Philharmonic
Society: world premiere*

Gwilym Simcock
Contours   *c17'*

Martinů
La revue de cuisine   *14'*

**Ronald van
Spaendonck** *clarinet*
Ilya Gringolts *violin*
Llŷr Williams *piano*
Tom Arthurs,
**Giuliano
Sommerhalder** *trumpets*
Richard Fairhurst *piano*
Gwilym Simcock *piano*
Aronowitz Ensemble
Helen Simons *bassoon*
Li-Wei *cello*

There will be no interval

*See 'Bright Young Things',
pages 48–51; 'New
Music', pages 54–60*

MONDAY 31 AUGUST

Proms Plus Royal College of Music
2.00pm Proms Family Orchestra The final Proms Family
Orchestra of the season. See pages 72–79 for how to sign up.
5.15pm Family Music Intro Bring your instrument along for a
chance to discover more about tonight's music.

7.00pm–c9.00pm

Sibelius
Symphony No. 1 in E minor   *40'*

interval

Duparc
L'invitation au voyage   *5'*

Extase (orch. Pierre de Bréville)   *4'*

Le manoir de Rosemonde   *3'*

Chanson triste   *4'*

Phidylé   *5'*

Ravel
Daphnis et Chloé – Suite No. 2   *18'*

Magdalena Kožená *mezzo-soprano*

Royal Concertgebouw Orchestra
Mariss Jansons *conductor*

Both Sibelius and Duparc stopped composing decades
before their deaths – three in the Finn's case, five in
the Frenchman's. The seven symphonies Sibelius left,
however, securely place him among the greatest
symphonists of the 20th century. Duparc left just
13 songs, yet each is a gem of textual subtlety and
melodic inspiration; lustrous-toned Czech mezzo-
soprano Magdalena Kožená sings her own selection.
Ravel's pastoral ballet *Daphnis et Chloé* – commissioned
by Diaghilev in 1909, the year he met Stravinsky –
was based on an ancient erotic novel; the Second
Suite begins with a sunrise and ends in an orgy.

Broadcast
RADIO Live on Radio 3
ONLINE Live and 'listen
again' options at
bbc.co.uk/proms

Broadcast
RADIO Live on Radio 3
ONLINE Live and 'listen
again' options at
bbc.co.uk/proms

Broadcast
RADIO Live on Radio 3
ONLINE Live and 'listen
again' options at
bbc.co.uk/proms

Broadcast
RADIO Live on Radio 3
ONLINE Live and 'listen
again' options at
bbc.co.uk/proms

Broadcast
RADIO Live on Radio 3
ONLINE Live and 'listen
again' options at bbc.co.uk/proms

TUESDAY 1 SEPTEMBER

Proms Plus 5.45pm, Royal College of Music
Proms Intro Rob Cowan talks to writer-broadcasters Hilary Finch and Lindsay Kemp about Haydn's symphonies.

7.30pm–c9.30pm

Haydn
Symphony No. 100 in G major, 'Military' *25'*

interval

Shostakovich
Symphony No. 10 in E minor *55'*

Royal Concertgebouw Orchestra
Mariss Jansons conductor

Mariss Jansons

In the second of their two Proms, Mariss Jansons and his Dutch orchestra bring Haydn's 'Military' Symphony, composed on his second visit to London, in 1794–5, at a time when England and Holland were allied with Austria against republican France. According to an early review, the slow movement – graphically portraying 'the hellish roar of war increase to a climax of horrid sublimity!' – was greeted with repeated cries of 'Encore!' in which 'the Ladies themselves could not forbear' to join. Shostakovich's Tenth – one of the composer's most popular symphonies, and a favourite of tonight's conductor and orchestra – intertwines the composer's personal motto theme with that of a student with whom he was infatuated. See 'Composers of the Year', pages 28–33

WEDNESDAY 2 SEPTEMBER

Proms Plus 5.45pm, Royal College of Music
Proms Intro Percussionist Colin Currie and Xenakis's friend and biographer, Nouritza Matossian join Martin Handley to discuss Xenakis and his works in tonight's Prom.
Edited version broadcast on Radio 3 during tonight's interval

7.30pm–c9.40pm

Xenakis
Nomos gamma *15'*

Rachmaninov
The Isle of the Dead *20'*

interval

Xenakis
Aïs *18'*

Shostakovich
Symphony No. 9 in E flat major *25'*

Leigh Melrose baritone
Colin Currie percussion

BBC Symphony Orchestra
David Robertson conductor

Colin Currie

With its 98 players dispersed among the audience, Xenakis's *Nomos gamma* should make a stunning Proms piece, not least as the final drumrolls from its eight percussionists ricochet around the Arena. Both *Aïs* – a searing setting of ancient Greek texts by Homer and Sappho, with a wildly wide-ranging vocal line – and Rachmaninov's Stygian tone-poem, composed a century ago, confront the transience of life and the finality of death, while Shostakovich's 1945 Ninth seems almost to laugh off the horrors of war. A former New Generation Artist, percussionist Colin Currie also appears in our NGA 10th-Anniversary Weekend (PCM 7) and in Prom 33. See 'Bright Young Things', pages 48–51

Promming places in the Arena will be very limited, but alternative spaces will be offered on the evening

PROM 63
Spotlight on ... David Robertson

Now at the end of his fourth season as Principal Guest Conductor of the BBC Symphony Orchestra, David Robertson is clearly enjoying his tenure. 'No matter how challenging the programmes are with this orchestra, there's a sense of lightness and joy in preparation and execution.' For his second of three Proms appearances this season he tackles a typically eclectic programme. Often dismissed by critics for his easy tune-spinning, Rachmaninov may seem an unusual choice for a conductor versed in some of the most challenging modern scores – such as the two Xenakis scores we hear tonight. But, Robertson says, '*The Isle of the Dead* is very unusual for a work of its time, having five-beat bars for much of the piece. Rachmaninov chose to give the feeling of undulation of the waves as you cross the river of death to the rocky isle. The constant rhythmic variety is both comforting and unsettling at the same time.'

And what of taking on the challenge of leading the musical celebrations for the Last Night? 'That's something I could never have dreamt of as an 18-year-old student at the Royal Academy of Music.' Is he daunted by the prospect of giving the customary Last Night speech? 'No – conductors should be seen and not heard, so I'll keep it short!'

Bavarian Radio (Jansons); Chris Dawes (Currie); Dan Dreyfus (Robertson)

THURSDAY 3 SEPTEMBER

Proms Plus 5.15pm, Royal College of Music
Proms Intro Tonight's conductor Vladimir Jurowski joins pianist Tamara Stefanovich in discussion with Sara Mohr-Pietsch.
Edited version broadcast on Radio 3 during tonight's first interval

Vladimir Jurowski

7.00pm–c10.00pm

Ibert
Bacchanale *10'*

Debussy
Jeux *18'*

interval

Mozart
Sonata in D major for two pianos, K448 *22'*

Zimmermann
Dialoge *17'*

interval

Brahms
Symphony No. 1 in C minor *45'*

Pierre-Laurent Aimard,
Tamara Stefanovich *pianos*

London Philharmonic Orchestra
Vladimir Jurowski *conductor*

Ibert's riotous 1956 *Bacchanale* was commissioned for the 10th anniversary of the BBC's Third Programme, forerunner of today's Radio 3. Tennis is only one of the 'games' played in Debussy's 1913 ballet, premiered by the Ballets Russes just two weeks before Stravinsky's *Rite of Spring* (Prom 38). Our multiple pianos focus continues with works by Mozart and Zimmermann – the latter of which quotes from both *Jeux* and Mozart's C major Concerto, K467. And the LPO, under its brilliant Principal Conductor, concludes with Brahms's hard-won First Symphony, composed under the burdensome shadow of Beethoven. *See 'A Frenzy of Fingerwork', pages 64–65*

Broadcast
RADIO Live on Radio 3
ONLINE Live and 'listen again' options at bbc.co.uk/proms
TV Broadcast at 7.30pm on BBC Four

FRIDAY 4 SEPTEMBER

WEEKEND PROMMING PASS • BEAT THE QUEUES AND SAVE MONEY (SEE PAGE 148)

Proms Plus 5.15pm, Royal College of Music
Proms Literary Festival Philosophers A. C. Grayling and Roger Scruton discuss how *fin-de-siècle* Viennese musicians such as Mahler were influenced by their philosopher contemporaries – and what we today owe to these Viennese thinkers. Susan Hitch hosts.
Edited version broadcast on Radio 3 during tonight's interval

7.00pm–c9.10pm

Ligeti
Atmosphères *9'*

Mahler
Kindertotenlieder *27'*

Schoenberg
Five Orchestral Pieces, Op. 16 *19'*

interval

R. Strauss
Also sprach Zarathustra *34'*

Matthias Goerne *baritone*

Gustav Mahler Jugendorchester
Jonathan Nott *conductor*

Following his appearance with the Bamberg SO (Prom 18), Jonathan Nott returns with the GMJO, with a pair of astronomically related works – Ligeti's nebular *Atmosphères* and Strauss's visionary *Also sprach Zarathustra* – famously used on the soundtrack of Stanley Kubrick's 1968 film *2001: A Space Odyssey*. (The astronomical theme continues in tonight's Late Night Prom.) Leading German baritone Matthias Goerne sings Mahler's harrowing set of meditations on infant mortality. Composed exactly a century ago and premiered at the 1912 Proms by Henry Wood, Schoenberg's Five Orchestral Pieces contain his first painterly experiments in shaping melodies from colours, not pitches.

Matthias Goerne

PROM 65
Spotlight on ... Jonathan Nott

Jonathan Nott rose through the ranks in Frankfurt, Wiesbaden and Lucerne before taking up his appointment as Principal Conductor of the Bamberg Symphony Orchestra in 2000. Alongside his Bamberg role, he also worked as Principal Conductor of the Ensemble Intercontemporain (succeeding David Robertson).

Though he has conducted most of the London orchestras, he is perhaps better known in Britain 'north of the border', where he and his Bamberg orchestra enjoyed a five-concert residency at the Edinburgh Festival in 2004. He made his Proms debut back in 1993 with the ASKO Ensemble, returning with the Bamberg SO for a well-received concert three years ago. Tonight's Prom plays both to his strengths and to those of the Gustav Mahler Jugendorchester.

'I made my London orchestral debut with *Also sprach Zarathustra*,' he recalls, 'and have conducted *Kindertotenlieder* on numerous occasions; most notably as part of a continuous first-half sequence that also began with Ligeti, the *Poème symphonique* for 100 metronomes.'

SAME-DAY SAVER
Book for both Proms 65 and 66 and save (see page 148)

Broadcast
RADIO Live on Radio 3
ONLINE Live and 'listen again' options at bbc.co.uk/proms
TV Broadcast at 7.30pm on BBC Four

FRIDAY 4 SEPTEMBER

10.15pm–c11.30pm

George Crumb
Night of the Four Moons   16'

Vox balaenae (Voice of the Whale)   18'

Ancient Voices of Children   25'

Hilary Summers *mezzo-soprano*

Nash Ensemble
Diego Masson *conductor*

Diego Masson

We celebrate the 80th birthday of George Crumb, a great American original whose hauntingly beautiful scores draw on many disparate traditions, often exploring novel performance techniques and involving symbolic or theatrical elements. Marking the 40th anniversary of the first manned mission to the Moon, *Night of the Four Moons* was actually composed during the Apollo 11 flight and ends – in a homage to Haydn's 'Farewell' Symphony – with the performers representing the 'Music of Mankind' leaving the stage to a lone cellist, portraying the 'Music of the Spheres'. Like *Ancient Voices of Children*, it sets verses by Federico García Lorca. In *Vox balaenae*, a flautist singing into the instrument imitates the cry of a humpback whale, while all three performers wear masks to efface their human presence.

SAME-DAY SAVER
Book for both Proms 65 and 66 and save (see page 148)

PROM 66
Spotlight on … George Crumb

American composer George Crumb (born 1929) has been fascinated with unusual combinations of instruments, and getting unusual, sometimes very delicate timbres from them, often by unorthodox playing methods. He also brings elements of theatre into the performance of his works, setting the players in motion or costume on the stage. And he is devoted to the works of Federico García Lorca, whose writings have provided the texts, or the ideas, for so many pieces.

All three aspects are reflected in tonight's Late Night Prom. *Night of the Four Moons*, from 1969, sets poetic fragments of Lorca to symbolise Crumb's own 'rather ambivalent feelings' about the contemporary Apollo moonshots. *Vox balaenae (Voice of the Whale)*, inspired by the songs of humpback whales, puts its three players into masks to suggest the sheer impersonality of nature when the human observer is removed. The highly expressive Lorca cycle *Ancient Voices of Children*, with its bravura vocal writing, was the piece that brought Crumb before a wider international audience: its passion, textural refinement and wide range of reference show his elusive art at its strongest.

Broadcast
RADIO Live on Radio 3
ONLINE Live and 'listen again' options at bbc.co.uk/proms

SATURDAY 5 SEPTEMBER

Proms Plus
2.00pm, Royal Geographical Society **Film** *God Rot Tunbridge Wells* (120', exempt from classification). Tony Palmer's film on Handel's life, starring Trevor Howard. Introduced by the director.
5.15pm, Royal College of Music **Proms Intro** Stephen Johnson in conversation with composer John McCabe about the process of composition and his Horn Concerto, with musicians from the Royal College of Music.

7.00pm–c9.05pm

Janáček, arr. Talich
The Cunning Little Vixen – suite   17'

John McCabe
Horn Concerto, 'Rainforest IV'   24'
London premiere

interval

Dvořák
Symphony No. 9 in E minor, 'From the New World'   42'

David Pyatt *horn*

BBC National Orchestra of Wales
Jac van Steen *conductor*

David Pyatt

Inspired by a comic strip about a frisky young lady-fox, Janáček's forest opera *The Cunning Little Vixen* is a heart-warming humanist hymn to nature's eternal cycle of life and death. Marking John McCabe's 70th birthday, the programme includes his Horn Concerto, which combines urban jazz with the sounds of the equatorial rainforests. The major musical memento of Dvořák's directorship of the National Conservatory of Music in New York, his Ninth Symphony was partly inspired by the scene of Minnehaha's forest funeral in Longfellow's *Hiawatha* but also exudes nostalgia for his – and the Vixen's – native Bohemian woods and fields. See 'New Music', pages 54–60

Broadcast
RADIO Live on Radio 3
ONLINE Live and 'listen again' options at bbc.co.uk/proms

SUNDAY 6 SEPTEMBER

Proms Plus
2.00pm–4.00pm, Royal Albert Hall **Proms Singing Day** Join the Proms Family Chorus; see page 79 for how to sign up.
4.45pm, Royal College of Music **Proms Intro** National Singing Ambassador Howard Goodall introduces Handel's *Messiah* and performances by Sing Up choirs.

6.30pm–c9.30pm

Handel
Messiah   c135'

Dominique Labelle *soprano*
Patricia Bardon *mezzo-soprano*
John Mark Ainsley *tenor*
Matthew Rose *bass*

Members of:
**City of Birmingham Symphony
Youth Chorus
Hallé Youth Choir
National Youth Choir of Great Britain
National Youth Choir of Wales
Quay Voices (The Sage Gateshead)
RSCM Millennium Youth Choir
Scunthorpe Co-operative Junior Choir**

**Northern Sinfonia
Nicholas McGegan** *conductor*

Nicholas McGegan

Our commemoration of the 250th anniversary of Handel's death reaches its climax with a large-scale, Royal Albert Hall-sized performance of *Messiah* – echoing the late-18th-century monster concerts that inspired Haydn's *Creation* (Prom 2) – Handel specialist Nicholas McGegan conducts a unique massed choir of young voices from around the UK, assembled under the direction of leading choral specialist Simon Halsey. *See 'Composers of the Year', pages 28–33*

There will be one interval

Broadcast
RADIO Live on Radio 3
ONLINE Live and 'listen again' options at bbc.co.uk/proms

PCM 19

MONDAY 7 SEPTEMBER

1.00pm–c2.00pm

Proms Chamber Music at Cadogan Hall

Purcell
Suite in G major – excerpts   5'
Hail, Bright Cecilia – ''Tis nature's voice'   5'
A New Ground   3'
Music for a while   4'
Suite in D major – excerpts   4'
Sweeter than roses   4'

Blow
Ode on the Death of Mr Henry Purcell   23'

Purcell
Evening Hymn   6'

Iestyn Davies *counter-tenor*
Simon Wall *tenor*

**Members of the Academy of Ancient Music
Richard Egarr** *harpsichord/director*

Iestyn Davies

The centrepiece of this recital – continuing our 350th-anniversary celebrations of Purcell's birth – is an affecting tribute to Purcell by his teacher and predecessor as organist of Westminster Abbey, John Blow. It sets Dryden's poem of the same name, which describes how 'the lark and linnet sing' but then fall silent at the appearance of 'the matchless man … our Orpheus'. A sequence of Purcell's solo songs and keyboard pieces and the deeply moving *Evening Hymn* complete this mix of mellifluous music. *See 'Composers of the Year', pages 28–33*

There will be no interval

Broadcast
RADIO Live on Radio 3
ONLINE Live and 'listen again' options at bbc.co.uk/proms

MONDAY 7 SEPTEMBER

Proms Plus 5.45pm, Royal College of Music
Proms Literary Festival Victorian Season: A. N. Wilson, author of *The Victorians*, and Steven Moffat, co-creator and Executive Producer of the BBC's new modern-day *Sherlock*, talk to Matthew Sweet about the enduring appeal of Sherlock Holmes and his special love of Mendelssohn.
Edited version broadcast on Radio 3 during tonight's interval

7.30pm–c9.45pm

Mendelssohn
Piano Concerto No. 1 in G minor, Op. 25   20'

interval

Mahler, compl. Cooke
Symphony No. 10   80'

Saleem Abboud Ashkar *piano*

**Leipzig Gewandhaus Orchestra
Riccardo Chailly** *conductor*

Continuing our bicentenary focus on Mendelssohn, Riccardo Chailly conducts the orchestra of which the composer himself was music director for the last 12 years of his life, in the concerto that he had completed in just three days, at the age of 22, in 1831. As soloist, we welcome back Saleem Abboud Ashkar, who made his Proms debut in 2003, playing Mozart's Concerto for three pianos with Shai Wosner (Prom 55), alongside Daniel Barenboim (Proms 48–50). Begun in the shadows of a failing marriage and failing health, Mahler's Tenth Symphony was left unfinished at his death but triumphantly premiered at the 1964 Proms in a 'performing version' prepared by the English

Riccardo Chailly

musicologist Deryck Cooke in collaboration with the late Berthold Goldschmidt, and later revised with the help of the composer-brothers Colin and David Matthews. *See 'Composers of the Year', pages 28–33*

Broadcast
RADIO Live on Radio 3
ONLINE Live and 'listen again' options at bbc.co.uk/proms

Randi Lynn Beach (McGegan); Vince Barone (Davies); Gert Mothes (Chailly)

TUESDAY 8 SEPTEMBER

Proms Plus 5.15pm, Royal College of Music
Proms Intro Sir Peter Maxwell Davies celebrates his 75th birthday and talks about composition and conducting with Martin Handley.
Edited version broadcast on Radio 3 during tonight's interval

7.00pm–c8.45pm

Mendelssohn
Overture 'The Hebrides' ('Fingal's Cave')   *10'*

Sir Peter Maxwell Davies
Violin Concerto No. 2   *c20'*
UK premiere

interval

Sibelius
Symphony No. 5 in E flat major*   *32'*

Daniel Hope *violin*

Royal Philharmonic Orchestra
Sir Peter Maxwell Davies *conductor*
Garry Walker *conductor**

Daniel Hope

Long a resident of the Orkney Islands, the Master of The Queen's Music, Sir Peter Maxwell Davies, celebrates his 75th birthday today by conducting Mendelssohn's sea-sprayed Hebridean overture and the UK premiere of his own new violin concerto, written for tonight's soloist, Daniel Hope, and commissioned by Mendelssohn's old orchestra, the Leipzig Gewandhaus, with which they give the work's premiere in August. Proms debutant Garry Walker, the RPO's Permanent Guest Conductor, completes the concert with Sibelius's surging 'swan hymn' symphony. *See 'Composers of the Year', pages 28–33; 'England at the Crossroads', pages 36–38; 'New Music', pages 54–60*

Broadcast
RADIO Live on Radio 3
ONLINE Live and 'listen again' options at bbc.co.uk/proms

TUESDAY 8 SEPTEMBER

10.00pm–c11.15pm

Sir Peter Maxwell Davies
Westerlings   *19'*

Solstice of Light   *50'*

Ed Lyon *tenor*
David Goode *organ*

BBC Singers
David Hill *conductor*

Sir Peter Maxwell Davies has written choral works throughout his career. To celebrate his 75th birthday today, the BBC Singers and their Chief Conductor David Hill devote their Late Night Prom exclusively to his music. The virtuosic and technically challenging *Westerlings*, premiered by the BBC Singers in 1977, consists of four songs to texts by the Orcadian poet George Mackay Brown, interspersed with wordless seascapes and capped by a concluding prayer in Old Norse, the ancient language of Sir Peter's adopted Orkney home. Also setting texts by Brown, *Solstice of Light* is a major cantata with organ, charting the whole history of the Orkneys and ending in an invocation to St Magnus, the islands' patron saint. *See 'England at the Crossroads', pages 36–38*

There will be no interval

Sir Peter Maxwell Davies

SAME-DAY SAVER
Book for both Proms 70 and 71 and save (see page 148)

Broadcast
RADIO Live on Radio 3
ONLINE Live and 'listen again' options at bbc.co.uk/proms

WEDNESDAY 9 SEPTEMBER

Proms Plus 5.45pm, Royal College of Music
Proms Composer Portrait Augusta Read Thomas, in conversation with Andrew McGregor, discusses her new violin concerto, and introduces performances of some of her chamber works.
Edited broadcast on Radio 3 following this evening's Prom

7.30pm–c9.45pm

Mendelssohn
A Midsummer Night's Dream – Overture and incidental music   *28'*

Augusta Read Thomas
Violin Concerto No. 3, 'Juggler in Paradise'   *21'*
BBC co-commission with Radio France, Mr & Mrs Bill Brown and National Symphony Orchestra, Washington DC: UK premiere

interval

Beethoven
Symphony No. 6 in F major, 'Pastoral'   *43'*

Frank Peter Zimmermann *violin*

BBC Symphony Orchestra
Jiří Bělohlávek *conductor*

We end our bicentenary salute to Mendelssohn with the magical *A Midsummer Night's Dream* overture that he wrote at the age of only 17, coupled with extracts from his later incidental music to Shakespeare's play. In Augusta Read Thomas's new Violin Concerto, the role of the 'juggler', rhapsodising his way through a pointillistic 'paradise' of bell sounds, is taken by Frank Peter Zimmermann, who premiered the work in Paris in January. And, to conclude, the BBC SO's Chief Conductor, Jiří Bělohlávek, takes the orchestra on a Beethovenian tour of the Austrian countryside. *See 'Composers of the Year', pages 28–33; 'New Music', pages 54–60*

Jiří Bělohlávek

Broadcast
RADIO Live on Radio 3
ONLINE Live and 'listen again' options at bbc.co.uk/proms

PROMS 73 & 74
Spotlight on …
Vienna Philharmonic Orchestra

As a concert-master of the Vienna Philharmonic, Volkhard Steude has played under the batons of some of the world's great conductors. This year, not one but two such figures appear at the Proms with this celebrated ensemble.

'Zubin Mehta and Nikolaus Harnoncourt both have very deep connections with our orchestra,' explains Steude. 'Mehta was very young when he conducted us for the first time, and he is now an Honorary Member. He has been familiar with our sound since the Karajan era [1957–64] – there is a sense of him having an overview of the recent history of our sound. Harnoncourt, even though he is now very experienced, to me still has the spirit of a younger revolutionary. He always brings a completely different view of the music – which is very sophisticated and smart, but also very stylish and natural. Maybe Mehta is more traditional – in a positive sense – whereas Harnoncourt is forming our new generation of players.'

Steude is modest about the Vienna Philharmonic's reputation as one of the world's foremost orchestras, but admits, 'That's what people say.' The reason, he thinks, 'comes from opera' – the Vienna Philharmonic being the luxury 'house' band for the Vienna State Opera. 'When you are playing both symphonic and opera works, your musical horizons are immediately broadened.'

THURSDAY 10 SEPTEMBER

Proms Plus 5.45pm, Royal College of Music
Proms Intro Petroc Trelawny is joined by Proms Director Roger Wright to look back over the 2009 Proms season.

7.30pm–c9.30pm

Haydn
Symphony No. 97 in C major   25'

interval

Schubert
Symphony No. 9 in C major, 'Great'   60'

Vienna Philharmonic Orchestra
Nikolaus Harnoncourt *conductor*

Period-performance pioneer Nikolaus Harnoncourt here makes his first ever Proms appearance in front of a modern symphony orchestra, conducting the incomparable Vienna Philharmonic in this season's last symphony by the 'father' of the form, 'Papa' Haydn (the bicentenary of whose death we mark this year). One of the first set of 12 'London' Symphonies, No. 97 was composed and premiered on Haydn's first visit to England in 1791–2. Only ever given a rough run-through in Vienna during the composer's all-too-short lifetime, Schubert's 'Great' C major was eventually accorded its posthumous premiere by another of this year's bicentenarians, Felix Mendelssohn, in 1839. *See 'Composers of the Year', pages 28–33*

Nikolaus Harnoncourt

Broadcast
RADIO Live on Radio 3
ONLINE Live and 'listen again' options at bbc.co.uk/proms
TV Live on BBC Four

FRIDAY 11 SEPTEMBER

Proms Plus 4.45pm, Royal College of Music
Proms Literary Festival Ian McMillan talks to critic John Mullan about the influential legacy of the novel *Don Quixote*, while actor Andrew Sachs brings to life the words of Cervantes's hero.
Edited version broadcast on Radio 3 during tonight's interval

6.30pm–c8.45pm

R. Strauss
Don Quixote   42'

interval

Brahms
Symphony No. 4 in E minor   45'

Christian Frohn *viola*
Tamás Varga *cello*

Vienna Philharmonic Orchestra
Zubin Mehta *conductor*

Zubin Mehta

In the second of its two Proms, the Vienna Philharmonic Orchestra is conducted by its distinguished long-term associate and Honorary Member, Zubin Mehta, one of the rare recipients of the orchestra's coveted badge of honour, the Nikisch Ring. Together they reinvigorate Strauss's quintessentially quixotic set of 'fantastic variations on a theme of knightly character'. Brahms's final symphony also ends in a vast set of variations, his gloriously late-Romantic take on a Baroque-style passacaglia, using a theme borrowed from a Bach cantata.

SAME-DAY SAVER
Book for both Proms 74 and 75 and save (see page 148)

Broadcast
RADIO Live on Radio 3
ONLINE Live and 'listen again' options at bbc.co.uk/proms

FRIDAY 11 SEPTEMBER

10.15pm–c11.30pm

Silk Road Ensemble with Yo-Yo Ma

Following its Proms debut in 2004, cellist Yo-Yo Ma's innovative and cross-cultural Silk Road Ensemble returns for a cornucopian Late Night Prom as part of its 10th-anniversary celebrations. The boundary-crossing offering explores yet more of the historical and contemporary musical links between East and West, inspired by the ancient trading route between China and Europe.

Silk Road Ensemble with Yo-Yo Ma

SAME-DAY SAVER
Book for both Proms 74 and 75 and save (see page 148)

Broadcast
RADIO Live on Radio 3
ONLINE Live and 'listen again' options at bbc.co.uk/proms

SATURDAY 12 SEPTEMBER

Proms Plus 5.45pm, Royal College of Music
Proms Intro Bring an instrument, or anything small that can create a sound, and join us in creating the first ever Proms Hoffnung-inspired Orchestra!

7.30pm–c10.30pm

Last Night of the Proms 2009

Oliver Knussen
Flourish with Fireworks   *4'*

Purcell, arr. Henry Wood
New Suite   *10'*

Purcell
Dido and Aeneas – 'Thy hand, Belinda … When I am laid in earth' (Dido's Lament); 'With drooping wings ye cupids come'   *10'*

Haydn
Trumpet Concerto in E flat major   *15'*

Mahler
Lieder eines fahrenden Gesellen   *18'*

Villa-Lobos
Chôros No. 10, 'Rasga o Coração'   *12'*

interval

Arnold
A Grand, Grand Overture   *8'*

Ketèlbey
In a Monastery Garden   *6'*

Piazzolla
Libertango   *4'*

Gershwin, arr. Barry Forgie
Shall We Dance – 'They can't take that away from me'   *c5'*
BBC commission: world premiere

BBC Proms Inspire composers
Fireworks Fanfares   *c3'*
world premiere

Handel
Music for the Royal Fireworks – excerpts   *c10'*

Arne, arr. Sargent
Rule, Britannia!   *8'*

Parry
Jerusalem   *2'*

Elgar
Pomp and Circumstance March No. 1   *8'*

The National Anthem   *2'*

Sarah Connolly *mezzo-soprano*
Alison Balsom *trumpet*

BBC Singers
BBC Symphony Chorus
BBC Symphony Orchestra
David Robertson *conductor*

The Last Night brings Alison Balsom, a former Radio 3 New Generation Artist, in a concerto by one anniversary composer (Haydn) and Sarah Connolly in a famous lament by another (Purcell), while a third (Handel) provides the main orchestral fireworks. Oliver Knussen's own *Flourish* (sparked by Stravinsky's *Fireworks* from the First Night) is complemented by new fanfares specially written by young Proms Inspire composers (see *pages 72–79*), which feature in our link-up with Last Night festivities around the country. We mark 50 years since the deaths of Albert Ketèlbey and Gerard Hoffnung (the latter in Arnold's uproarious piece including parts for vacuum cleaners, floor polishers and rifles, written for the first Hoffnung Music Festival in 1956). And the BBC SO's David Robertson presides for the first time over the massed forces on stage and in the audience.

Sarah Connolly

Alison Balsom

Broadcast
RADIO Live on Radio 3
ONLINE Live and 'listen again' options at bbc.co.uk/proms
TV First half live on BBC Two; second half live on BBC One

BBC PROMS IN THE PARK

ns&i

Event supporters

The Last Night magic, live in the open air!

Each of the Proms in the Park events is centred around a live concert with high-profile artists and presenters, culminating in a live BBC Big Screen link-up to the Royal Albert Hall. So gather together your friends, pack a picnic and get ready for a fabulous night out.

If there isn't a Proms in the Park near you, you can join the party via one of the BBC Big Screens around the country: Bradford (Centenary Square), Bristol (Millennium Square), Cardiff (The Hayes), Derby (Market Place), Hull (Queen Victoria Square), Leeds (Millennium Square), Liverpool (Clayton Square), Manchester (Exchange Square), Middlesbrough (Centre Square), Norwich (Chapelfield Plain), Plymouth (Armada Way), Portsmouth (Guildhall Square), Rotherham (All Saints Square), Swansea (Castle Square), Swindon (Wharf Green), Waltham Forest (Walthamstow Town Square) and other new screens currently being commissioned across the UK.

All this year's concerts are broadcast live across BBC Radio and Television (see listings for details). Highlights of the Proms in the Park events will be included as part of the live coverage of the Last Night of the Proms on BBC One and BBC Two, while digital TV viewers can choose between watching the concert inside the Royal Albert Hall and the various Proms in the Park events taking place across the country.

Note that all BBC Proms in the Park events are outdoors and tickets are unreserved. The use of chairs is discouraged since it obstructs the view of others, but if you find it necessary because of limited mobility, please be considerate to your neighbours. In the interest of safety, please do not bring glass items, barbeques or flaming torches.

The Proms in the Park events are supported by National Savings and Investments.

SATURDAY 12 SEPTEMBER

Katherine Jenkins *mezzo-soprano*
Sir Terry Wogan *presenter*

Royal Choral Society
BBC Concert Orchestra
Martin Yates *conductor*

with thanks to

THE ROYAL PARKS

Katherine Jenkins   Sir Terry Wogan

Join in the Last Night celebrations in Hyde Park with Sir Terry Wogan and a host of internationally acclaimed stars, including Katherine Jenkins, accompanied by Proms in the Park favourites the BBC Concert Orchestra, conducted by Martin Yates.

The party gets under way with BBC Radio 2 presenter Ken Bruce, as well as highlights from *One Night of Queen* with Gary Mullen and The Works.

Gates open 4.00pm; entertainment from 5.30pm
For corporate hospitality facilities, call Charles Webb on 01484 437422, or visit sellershospitality.com

Tickets: £25.00 (under-3s free); Family and Friends ticket offer: buy 7 tickets and get the 8th free. Tickets now available: online via bbc.co.uk/proms (transaction fees vary, see website for details); by phone from the Royal Albert Hall on 0845 401 5040* (9.00am–9.00pm, £2.75 transaction fee) or from See Tickets on 0844 412 4630* (£2.00 transaction fee); in person at the Royal Albert Hall (Door 12, 9.00am–9.00pm, no transaction fee); and by post using the Advance Booking Form (page 153), 20 April – 18 May. *Calls cost up to 5p per minute (0844 numbers) and 4p per minute (0845 numbers) from a BT landline (plus a one-off connection charge of up to 8p). Charges from mobiles and other networks may be considerably higher.

Broadcast
RADIO Live on BBC Radio 2
ONLINE Live and 'listen again' options
TV Live via the red button on BBC Television

SATURDAY 12 SEPTEMBER

Nicola Benedetti *violin*
Jamie MacDougall *presenter*

NYCoS National Girls Choir
BBC Scottish Symphony Orchestra
Robert Ziegler *conductor*

BBC Proms in the Park returns to Glasgow Green for another spectacular evening of music and song, as we celebrate the Last Night of the Proms in true Scottish style. Join us for an unforgettable concert featuring the BBC Scottish Symphony Orchestra and some very special guests in this year of Homecoming Scotland, including violinist Nicola Benedetti.

Nicola Benedetti

Tickets are free and available from 1 June. For more details, visit bbc.co.uk/tickets or phone 0370 901 1227. (Standard geographic charges apply and calls may be included in your telecom provider's call package. Charges from mobiles may be higher.)

Glasgow Green

Broadcast
RADIO Live on BBC Radio Scotland
ONLINE Live and 'listen again' options
TV Live via the red button on BBC Television (satellite and cable only)

SATURDAY 12 SEPTEMBER

Sir James Galway *flute*
Noel Thompson *presenter*

Ulster Orchestra

Hillsborough Castle

Sir James Galway and a line-up of international soloists join the Ulster Orchestra for this year's BBC Proms in the Park in the grounds of one of Northern Ireland's most picturesque historic estates. The concert will be introduced by BBC Northern Ireland's Noel Thompson.

Concert begins 8.00pm

Tickets are free and available from 1 June. For more details, visit bbc.co.uk/ni/tickets or phone 0370 901 1227. (Standard geographic charges apply and calls may be included in your telecom provider's call package. Charges from mobiles may be higher.)

Sir James Galway   Noel Thompson

Broadcast
RADIO Live on BBC Radio Ulster
ONLINE Live and 'listen again' options
TV Live on BBC Four and via the red button on BBC Television (satellite and cable only)

SATURDAY 12 SEPTEMBER

BBC Philharmonic
Stephen Bell *conductor*

Thousands of music-lovers will bring picnics, flags and their finest singing voices to fill Salford's beautiful and historic Buile Hill Park for an unforgettable evening of popular tunes and rousing classics. Led by the BBC Philharmonic and well-loved conductor Stephen Bell, and featuring special guests, the night is sure to conclude with a bang – a spectacular fireworks display lighting up the city's skies.

Stephen Bell

Tickets are priced at £10 (Salford residents only) and £15. For more details, visit www.visitsalford.info or phone 0161 848 8601.

Buile Hill Park

Broadcast
RADIO Live on BBC Radio Manchester

SATURDAY 12 SEPTEMBER

Elin Manahan Thomas *soprano*

BBC National Chorus of Wales
BBC National Orchestra of Wales
Grant Llewellyn *conductor*

Singleton Park celebrates an evening of music and song in its seventh BBC Proms in the Park from Swansea.

The BBC National Orchestra and Chorus of Wales with conductor Grant Llewellyn and guest soloists bring an evening of rousing choruses and orchestral favourites to the city and link up with the Royal Albert Hall and parks across the UK for the traditional Last Night celebrations. A Community Stage will host pre-concert performances, and audience-participation singing and fireworks will make it a night to remember.

Gates open 4.30pm; entertainment from 6.00pm

Tickets: £8.00 in advance. £10.00 on the day (under-12s free with accompanying adult). Advance telephone bookings will be taken until the box offices close on 11 September – see details below. Available from the BBC National Orchestra of Wales Audience Line on 03700 101051*. Lines are open Monday–Friday 9.00am–9.00pm and 9.00am–5.00pm on Saturdays. Tickets are also available in person or by phone from the Grand Theatre, Singleton Street, Swansea (01792 475715). Lines are open Monday–Saturday 9.30am–8.00pm, 9.30am–6.00pm on non-performance days. Also available online at bbc.co.uk/proms. *Standard geographic charges apply and calls may be included in your telecom provider's call package. Charges from mobiles may be higher.

Elin Manahan Thomas

Broadcast
RADIO Live on BBC Radio Wales
ONLINE Live and 'listen again' options
TV Live via the red button on BBC Television (satellite and cable only)

HOW TO BOOK

ADVANCE BOOKING Monday 20 April – Monday 18 May
Online and by post

To take advantage of the Advance Booking period – and enjoy your best chance of securing the seats you want – you must use the online ticket request system on the Proms website or the Advance Booking Form (*page 153*).

Online and postal bookings received *before* Monday 20 April will be treated as if they had arrived on that date, and will not therefore be processed in the order in which they are received. Bookings received *during* the Advance Booking period (Monday 20 April – Monday 18 May) will be processed in date order. Bookings received *after* Monday 18 May will be treated as General Bookings, and dealt with from Tuesday 26 May.

If you have any queries about how to complete the Advance Booking Form, call the Royal Albert Hall Box Office on 0845 401 5040*.

Please note that the Express Booking system has been discontinued.

Online: bbc.co.uk/proms
By post: BBC Proms, Box Office,
Royal Albert Hall, London SW7 2AP

GENERAL BOOKING Opens Tuesday 26 May
Online, by phone or in person

Online: Book online at bbc.co.uk/proms where you can select your own seat.

Telephone: 0845 401 5040*
Please note that calls may be monitored for training and quality-control purposes

In person: The Royal Albert Hall Box Office is located at Door 12 and is open 9.00am–9.00pm daily. Note that no booking fee applies to tickets bought in person at the Royal Albert Hall.

FOUR STEPS TO SUCCESS …

For those 'must-see' concerts this summer, remember these four steps for your best chance of securing tickets for the most popular Proms:

1 BOOK IN ADVANCE
Applying for tickets during the Advance Booking period (Monday 20 April – Monday 18 May) will give you the best chance of securing the tickets you want. Use the online ticket request system at bbc.co.uk/proms or the Advance Booking Form on page 153 (and use the guide on page 152 to help you fill it out). While Advance Booking does not guarantee that you will get the tickets you want, it does give you the best chance of securing tickets for the most popular concerts.

2 BE FLEXIBLE
When using the Advance Booking Form or the online ticket request system, check the appropriate 'Higher/Lower Alternative Price Tickets' box next to each selected concert. Seats in some price bands at the most popular concerts will sell out during the Advance Booking period. You can increase your chances of getting tickets to those concerts by agreeing to accept lower- or higher-priced alternatives, should the tickets in your selected price band be unavailable.

3 KEEP TRYING …
Even if your initial application is unsuccessful, keep trying bbc.co.uk/proms or the Royal Albert Hall Box Office. As with other venues, returns occasionally become available. Also, many boxes and some seats at the Royal Albert Hall are privately owned, and these seats may also be returned for general sale in the period leading up to the concert. The Royal Albert Hall does not operate a waiting list.

4 IF YOU CAN'T SIT, STAND!
Up to 1,400 standing places are available for every concert at the Royal Albert Hall, so if you arrive early enough on the day of the concert you have a very good chance of getting in.

HOW TO PROM

What is Promming?

The popular tradition of Promming is central to the unique and informal atmosphere of the BBC Proms at the Royal Albert Hall.

Up to 1,400 standing places are available for each Proms concert. The traditionally low prices allow you to enjoy world-class concerts for just £5.00 each (or even less with a Season Ticket or Weekend Promming Pass). There are two standing areas: the Arena, located directly in front of the stage, and the Gallery, running round the top of the Hall. All spaces are unreserved.

Day Prommers

Over 500 Arena and Gallery tickets (priced £5.00) go on sale 30 minutes before doors open. These tickets cannot be booked in advance, so even if all seats have been sold, you always have a good chance of getting in (though early queuing is advisable for the more popular concerts). You must buy your ticket in person, and must pay by cash.

Arena and Gallery tickets are available at Door 11 (Arena) and Door 10 (Gallery), not at the Box Office.

Wheelchair-users who wish to Prom (Gallery only) should queue in the same way but will be redirected to Door 8 once their ticket is purchased. For further information for disabled concert-goers, see page 159.

If you are in doubt about where to go, Royal Albert Hall stewards will point you in the right direction.

Prommers' Season Tickets

Frequent Prommers can save money by purchasing Arena or Gallery Season Tickets covering either the whole Proms season (including the Last Night) or only the first or second half (ie Proms 1–38 or Proms 39–75, excluding the Last Night).

Season Ticket-holders benefit from:
- guaranteed entrance (until 10 minutes before each concert)
- great savings – prices can work out at less than £2.25 per concert
- guaranteed entrance to the Last Night for Whole Season Ticket-holders and special access to a reserved allocation of Last Night tickets for Half Season Ticket-holders (see page 149).

Please note that Season Ticket-holders arriving at the Hall less than 10 minutes before a concert are not guaranteed entry and may be asked, in certain circumstances, to join the day queue.

Season Tickets are non-transferable and two passport-sized photographs must be provided before tickets can be issued. Season Tickets are not valid for concerts at Cadogan Hall.

For further details and prices of Season Tickets (see page 151). You can also buy Weekend Promming Passes (see page 148).

Proms at Cadogan Hall

For Cadogan Hall Promming, PCM Series Pass, NGA Day Tickets and booking information, see page 158.

Please note that numbered slips will be available from 8.00am on Saturday 29, Sunday 30 and Monday 31 August at the Royal Albert Hall for Prommers wishing to reserve their place in the Royal Albert Hall queue and also attend NGA anniversary concerts at Cadogan Hall.

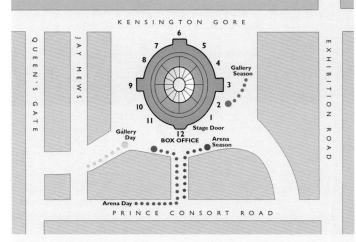

Where to Queue

- ● **Arena Day Queue**
  Enter by Door 11

- ● **Arena Season Queue**
  Enter by Door 1

- ○ **Gallery Day Queue**
  Enter by Door 10

- ● **Gallery Season Queue**
  Enter by Door 2

Join the Prommers and soak up the unique Proms atmosphere. Over 500 tickets (at just £5.00 each) are available at the door for every concert at the Royal Albert Hall

Chris Christodoulou

SPECIAL OFFERS

SAME-DAY SAVER

Same-Day Savers

Book seats for more than one concert on the same day, and save £4.00 per ticket for the later concert.

This offer applies to performances at the Royal Albert Hall only. Please note that Proms 13, 21 and 23 are excluded from this offer, and it is not valid for Arena, Gallery and Circle (Restricted View) price bands. See page 151 for price band information.

Kids Go Half-Price

The Proms are a great way to discover live music, and we encourage anyone over 5 years old to attend. Tickets for under-16s can be purchased at half-price in any seating area for all Proms except the Last Night (Prom 76).

Note that the family concerts on Sunday 26 July (Prom 13 – free concert), Saturday 1 August (Prom 21) and Sunday 2 August (Prom 23) are expressly designed to introduce young children to concert-going.

Great Savings for Groups

Groups of 10 or more can claim a 10% discount (5% for C band concerts) on the price of Centre/Side Stalls or Front/Rear Circle tickets (excluding the Last Night). See page 151 for price band information.

For more information, call the Group Booking Information Line on 020 7838 3108.

Please note that group purchases cannot be made online during the General Booking period.

Proms Chamber Music Series Pass and New Generation Artists 10th-Anniversary Weekend Day Tickets

Attend seven PCM concerts for just £30.00 with the PCM Series Pass; and see four concerts for the price of three at the New Generation Artists 10th-Anniversary Weekend at Cadogan Hall (*see page 158*).

Proms in the Park Friends and Family Group Ticket

Make a real party of the Last Night in Hyde Park – buy 7 tickets and get the 8th ticket free.

Weekend Promming Pass

Beat the queues at the weekend and save money! Promming is an essential part of the character of the BBC Proms. In addition to discounted tickets, the Weekend Promming Pass offers guaranteed access up to 10 minutes before start-time to the Arena or Gallery standing areas for all concerts in the Royal Albert Hall on Fridays, Saturdays and Sundays (excluding Proms 21, 23, 74, 75 and 76). Passes can be purchased in advance, online or by post (using the Advance Booking Form) and – from Tuesday 26 May – by phone or in person at the Royal Albert Hall Box Office. Passes are available up to 6.00pm on the day they start (5.30pm on 21 & 28 August and 4 September). Prices vary for each weekend depending on the number of concerts covered – see box below.

Note that Weekend 2 *includes* the FREE Family Prom (Prom 13), Weekend 3 *excludes* the two Family Proms (Proms 21 & 23), Weekend 6 includes Bank Holiday Monday (24 August); and there is no pass covering Proms 74–76. Weekend Promming Passes are not valid for concerts at Cadogan Hall.

Passes are non-transferable and signature ID may be requested upon entry. Purchase of a Weekend Promming Pass does not guarantee entry to the Last Night, but tickets may be counted towards the 'Five-Concert Rule' (see *opposite*) in conjunction with further Passes or Day Ticket stubs.

Note that you may purchase a maximum of four passes per weekend. Weekend Promming Passes are subject to availability.

For Whole and Half-Season Tickets, see page 151.

Weekend Promming Pass prices		
Weekend 1	Proms 1 – 4	£17.50
Weekend 2	Proms 10 – 14	£17.50
Weekend 3	Proms 20, 22 & 24	£12.50
Weekend 4	Proms 30 – 33	£17.50
Weekend 5	Proms 39 – 42	£17.50
Weekend 6	Proms 48 – 51	£17.50
Weekend 7	Proms 57 – 61	£22.50
Weekend 8	Proms 65 – 68	£17.50

THE LAST NIGHT

Owing to the huge demand for Last Night tickets, special booking arrangements apply. The best chance of purchasing tickets for the Last Night of the Proms is through the Advance Booking system.

Advance Booking for the Last Night

The Five-Concert Rule

In order to apply for any tickets for the Last Night during the Advance Booking period (20 April – 18 May), you must book for at least five other concerts at the Royal Albert Hall in the 2009 season. (*Please note that Prom 13 and concerts at Cadogan Hall do not count towards the Five-Concert Rule.*)

Book one ticket in the same seating area for at least five other concerts and you can apply at the same time for a single ticket in the same seating area for the Last Night. For example, book one ticket in the Choir for five concerts, and you can apply for one ticket in the Choir for the Last Night.

Book two *or more* tickets in the same seating area for at least five other concerts in the 2009 season and you can apply at the same time for a maximum of *two* tickets in the same seating area for the Last Night (*ie* whether you book two or 22 Stalls tickets for five concerts, you can still apply for only two Stalls tickets for the Last Night).

Note that if you book tickets for at least five other concerts but in different seating areas, you will be allocated Last Night seats in the area of the majority of your bookings (unless you specify that lower-priced tickets are desired).

We regret that, if the Last Night is sold out by the time your application is processed, no refunds for other tickets purchased will be payable.

General Booking for the Last Night

Once General Booking opens (Tuesday 26 May), the Five-Concert Rule no longer applies. Last Night tickets have usually sold out by this stage, but returns occasionally become available for sale, so it is always worth checking with the Box Office.

Please note that for all Last Night bookings, only one application (for a maximum of two tickets) can be made per household.

Promming at the Last Night

Day Prommers and Weekend Promming

Pass-holders who have attended five or more other concerts (in either the Arena or the Gallery) can buy one ticket each for the Last Night (priced £5.00) on presentation of their used tickets at the Box Office on or after Monday 20 July (subject to availability).

Season Ticket-holders Whole Season Tickets include admission to the Last Night. A limited allocation of Last Night places is also reserved for Half-Season Ticket-holders. Holders of First Half Season Tickets can buy one ticket each (priced £5.00) at the Box Office from Monday 20 July (subject to availability). Holders of Second-Half Season Tickets can buy tickets in the same way from Tuesday 18 August (subject to availability).

Queuing Whole Season Ticket-holders and other Prommers with Last Night tickets are guaranteed entrance until 10 minutes before the concert. All Prommers (Day or Season) with Last Night tickets should queue on the South Steps, west side (Arena) or the top of Bremner Road, left side (Gallery).

Sleeping Out There has long been a tradition of Prommers with Last Night tickets sleeping out overnight to secure their preferred standing place inside the Hall. The official queues will form at 4.00pm on the last Friday of the season. Those also wishing to attend Proms 74 and/or 75 will be given numbered slips to reserve their places in the queue, but must return in person immediately after the end of the concert(s).

On the Night Standing tickets are usually still available on the Last Night itself (priced £5.00, one per person). No previous ticket purchases are necessary. Just join the queue on the South Steps, east side (Arena) or the top of Bremner Road, right side (Gallery) during the afternoon and you may well be lucky.

Last Night Ballot 2009

One hundred Centre Stalls seats (priced £82.50 each) for the Last Night of the Proms at the Royal Albert Hall will be allocated by ballot. The 'Five-Concert Rule' does not apply, and no other ticket purchases are necessary. Only one application (for a maximum of two tickets) may be made per household.

If you would like to apply for tickets by ballot, please complete the official Ballot Form on the back of this slip and send it by post only – to arrive no later than Thursday 9 July – to:

**BBC Proms Ballot,
Box Office,
Royal Albert Hall,
London SW7 2AP**

Note that the Proms Ballot application is completely separate from other Proms booking procedures. Envelopes should be clearly addressed to 'BBC Proms Ballot' and should contain only the official Ballot Form, together with your cheque or credit/debit card details. If sending a cheque, please also enclose an SAE so that it can be returned to you if your application is unsuccessful. Successful applicants will be notified by post within two weeks of the ballot, which takes place on Friday 10 July.

This form is also available to download from bbc.co.uk/proms; or call 020 7765 5407 to receive a copy of this form by post.

The personal information given on this form will not be used for any purpose by the BBC or the Royal Albert Hall other than this ballot.

Last Night Ballot 2009

Title

Initial

Surname

Address

Postcode

Country

Daytime tel.

Please tick the appropriate boxes

☐ I wish to apply for one ticket (£82.50)

☐ I wish to apply for two tickets (£165.00)

☐ I enclose a cheque made payable to 'Royal Albert Hall' and an SAE. (Cheques will be returned to unsuccessful applicants within two weeks of the ballot.)

☐ Please debit my Visa/Amex/Mastercard/Solo/Maestro card

Start date ☐☐ / ☐☐   Issue no. ☐☐

Expiry date ☐☐ / ☐☐   Maestro only

Security code (CVV no.) ☐☐☐☐

last 3 digits on back of card (Visa/Mastercard); 4 digits on front (Amex)

Signature

CHOOSE YOUR SEAT

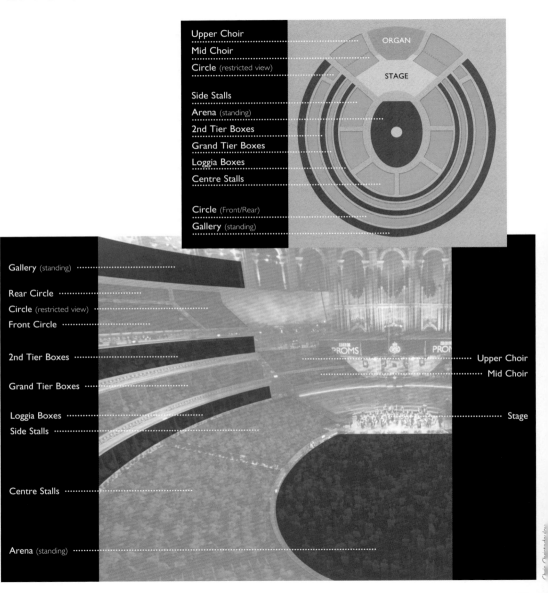

Upper Choir
Mid Choir
Circle (restricted view)
Side Stalls
Arena (standing)
2nd Tier Boxes
Grand Tier Boxes
Loggia Boxes
Centre Stalls
Circle (Front/Rear)
Gallery (standing)

ORGAN
STAGE

Gallery (standing)
Rear Circle
Circle (restricted view)
Front Circle
2nd Tier Boxes
Grand Tier Boxes
Loggia Boxes
Side Stalls
Centre Stalls
Arena (standing)

Upper Choir
Mid Choir
Stage

TICKET PRICES

Seats

Concerts fall into one of seven price bands, indicated above each concert listing on pages 106–143.

	A	B	C	D	E	F	G
Centre Stalls	£26.00	£36.00	£44.00	£15.00	£17.50	£82.50	
Side Stalls	£24.00	£32.00	£40.00	£15.00	£17.50	£80.00	
Grand Tier Boxes	£35.00	£44.00	£54.00	£15.00	£17.50	£90.00	
12 seats, price per seat	(As most Grand Tier Boxes are privately owned, availability is limited)						**ALL SEATS £12.00 (UNDER-16s £6.00)**
Loggia Boxes 8 seats, price per seat	£30.00	£40.00	£48.00	£15.00	£17.50	£85.00	
2nd Tier Boxes 5 seats, price per seat	£20.00	£25.00	£35.00	£15.00	£17.50	£72.50	
Mid Choir	£18.00	£21.00	£30.00	N/A	N/A	£60.00	
Upper Choir	£16.00	£19.00	£26.00	N/A	N/A	£55.00	
Front Circle	£14.00	£17.00	£22.00	£10.00	£14.00	£55.00	
Rear Circle	£11.00	£13.00	£17.00	£10.00	£14.00	£45.00	
Circle (restricted view)	£7.00	£8.00	£12.00	N/A	N/A	£25.00	

Promming (standing)

Standing places are available in the Arena and Gallery on the day for £5.00 *(see page 147)*

Season Tickets	**Dates**	**Arena**	**Gallery**
Whole Season (Proms 1–76)	17 July – 12 September	**£190.00**	**£170.00**
Half-Season Tickets			
First Half (Proms 1–38)	17 July – 13 August	**£110.00**	**£95.00**
Second Half (Proms 39–75)	14 August – 12 September	**£110.00**	**£95.00**

Please note that booking fees apply to all postal, telephone and online bookings (for details, see Booking Form). Unwanted tickets may be exchanged for tickets to other Proms concerts (subject to availability). A fee of £1.00 per ticket will be charged for this service. Telephone the Royal Albert Hall Box Office (0845 401 5040*) for further details.

BBC Proms in the Park, Hyde Park, London, Saturday 12 September

All tickets £25.00 (for further details of this and other Proms in the Park events around the country, see pages 144–145)
Friends and Family Group Ticket: buy 7 tickets and get the 8th ticket free.

Other Information

Disabled Concert-Goers
See page 159 for details of special discounts, access and facilities.

Privately Owned Seats
A high proportion of boxes, as well as 650 Stalls seats, are privately owned. Unless returned by owners, these seats are not usually available for sale.

Season Tickets
Season Tickets and Proms Chamber Music Series Passes can be booked online or by post from Monday 20 April and by phone or in person at the Royal Albert Hall Box Office from Tuesday 26 May. For postal bookings, complete the special section of the Booking Form *(page 153)*. Please note that two passport-sized photographs must be provided for each season ticket or pass before it can be issued.

Proms at Cadogan Hall
For booking information on the Proms Chamber Music series, see page 158.

HOW TO FILL IN THE BOOKING FORM

- **Choose the concerts** you want to go to and where you want to sit.

- **Enter the number of tickets** you require for each concert under your chosen seating area (adult tickets on the white squares, under-16s on the blue).

- **Add up the value of tickets** requested referring to the price bands on page 151, and enter the amount in the 'Sub-total' column.

- **If claiming any special offers** (see page 148) or disabled concert-goers' discounts (see page 159), enter the total value of discounts claimed for each concert in the red 'Discount' column. Then subtract the value of the discount from the 'Sub-total' and enter the 'Total' at the end of the row (adding in any car parking fee, if applicable).

- **In case the tickets you request are not available**, you can opt to receive lower- or higher-priced alternatives by ticking the appropriate box next to each concert. Ticking one or both of these boxes increases your chances of securing tickets for the most popular concerts.

Booking Queries

If you have any queries about how to fill in the Booking Form, call the Box Office on 0845 401 5040*, open 9.00am–9.00pm daily.

*Calls cost up to 4p per minute from a BT landline (plus a one-off connection charge of up to 8p). Charges from mobiles and other networks may be considerably higher

Online Booking

For details of how to book online, visit bbc.co.uk/proms
Note that once General Booking opens (on Tuesday 26 May), online customers will be able to choose their own seats.

Checklist

Before posting your booking form, please check that you have:

- [ ] Filled in your name at the top of both sides.

- [ ] Indicated whether you will accept lower- and/or higher-priced tickets.

- [ ] Entered your data protection preferences.

- [ ] Enclosed two passport-sized photographs for each Proms Season Ticket or PCM Series Pass applied for.

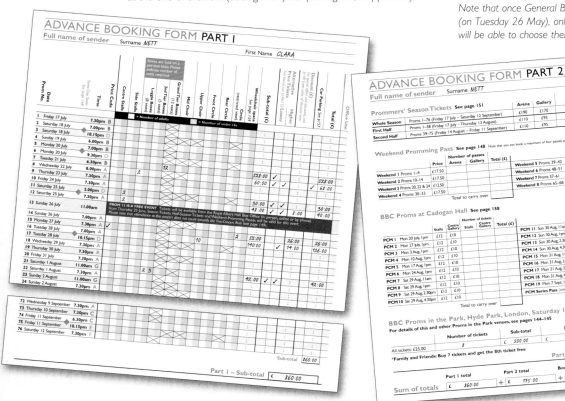

ROYAL ALBERT HALL
Kensington Gore, London SW7 2AP *(see map, page 160).* www.royalalberthall.com

Leith's are the official caterers at the Royal Albert Hall, providing a wide range of food and drink within the bars, restaurants and boxes.

Restaurants

Café Consort is fully licensed and offers a menu of contemporary dishes. Post-concert drinks and light meals are also available on selected dates. Further details will be sent with your tickets and will also be available from www.royalalberthall.com

Coda is a stylish restaurant offering an elegant dining experience with a modern British menu.

The **East Arena Foyer** serves a selection of light dishes.

The restaurants open two hours before the performance, except the Café Consort, which opens two and a half hours beforehand. Tables should be booked in advance, except for the East Arena Foyer. Call the Box Office on 0845 401 5040* to make your reservation.

The **Elgar Restaurant** will be closed this summer for refurbishment.

Bars

Bars are located on all but the Gallery level, offering a full range of drinks, sandwiches, confectionery and ice cream. The East Arena Foyer, North Circle Bar and Champagne Bar open two hours prior to each concert. All other bars open 45 minutes before the start of the performance.

Interval orders

Interval orders can be arranged from any bar. Please ask any member of bar staff.

Box hospitality

If you have seats in one of the Hall's boxes, you can pre-order catering. Please call 020 7589 5666 for details. Orders should then be placed in writing at least two working days before the concert that you are attending.

Please note Leith's do not permit the consumption of your own food and drink in the Hall. In the interests of health and safety, only cold soft drinks in closed plastic containers are allowed into the auditorium. Glasses and bottles are permitted in boxes, as part of box hospitality ordered through Leith's.

Café Consort: one of many places to eat and drink at the Royal Albert Hall

Car parking

A limited number of parking spaces, priced £8.00 each, is available from 6.00pm (or one hour before weekend matinee concerts) in the Imperial College car park (Prince Consort or Exhibition Road entrances). These can be booked using the Advance Booking Form (*page 153*), online (from 20 April) or by calling the Box Office on 0845 401 5040*, open 9.00am–9.00pm daily (from 26 May). Please note that, if attending both early-evening and late-night concerts, only one parking fee is payable.

Doors open 45 minutes before the start of each concert (earlier for restaurant and bar access) and 30 minutes before each late-night concert.

Latecomers will not be admitted into the auditorium unless or until there is a suitable break in the music. There is a video screen in the Door 6 foyer with a digital audio relay.

Bags and coats may be left in the cloakrooms at Door 9 (ground level) and at basement level beneath Door 6. For reasons of safety and comfort, only small bags are permitted in the Arena.

Security In the interests of safety, bags may be searched upon entry.

Children under 5 Out of consideration for both audience and artists, children under the age of 5 are not allowed in the auditorium.

Dress code Come as you are: there is no dress code at the Proms.

Mobile phones and watch alarms should be turned off.

The use of cameras, video cameras and recording equipment is strictly forbidden.

Tours of the Royal Albert Hall

Tours run every day, except Wednesdays, and last approximately one hour. To book and to check availability, please call 020 7838 3105. Tickets cost £8.00 per person, with a number of concessions available.

Royal Albert Hall shop

The Royal Albert Hall shop, offering a selection of Proms and Royal Albert Hall gifts and souvenirs, is located inside the South Porch at Door 12. The shop is open daily from 10.00am to 6.00pm. Proms merchandise can also be purchased at the Door 6 foyer during performance times.

CADOGAN HALL

5 Sloane Terrace, London SW1X 9DQ *(see map, page 160)*
www.cadoganhall.com

Proms Chamber Music returns for another lunchtime series in the light and airy surroundings of this superb hall in the heart of Chelsea. Its warm and intimate acoustic is ideal for a wide range of music and this year there are more concerts than ever, with a special weekend celebrating the 10th anniversary of BBC Radio 3's New Generation Artists scheme *(see page 48)*. Distinguished former NGA artists the Belcea Quartet and Llŷr Williams also feature in two other concerts, with music inspired by Proms anniversary composers Purcell and Handel. Iestyn Davies, Richard Egarr and members of the Academy of Ancient Music also honour Purcell, as do the strings of the Scottish Ensemble, who also premiere a brilliant new work by John Woolrich. Joshua Bell, Steven Isserlis and Dénes Várjon focus on Mendelssohn, another anniversary composer, while Susan Graham and Malcolm Martineau revel in the seductive delights of French song. And the series begins with a flourish as The Cardinall's Musick celebrates the 500th anniversary of the coronation of King Henry VIII, including a song by the King himself that sets the tone for the whole season: 'Pastyme with good companye'!

All Proms Chamber Music concerts are broadcast live on BBC Radio 3. PCMs 1–5 & 19 will be repeated the following Saturday at 2.00pm, and PCM 6 will be repeated on Saturday 6 September at 2.00pm

Doors open at 12 noon; entrance to the auditorium will be from half an hour before start-time

Proms Chamber Music at Cadogan Hall – ticket prices

**Stalls: £12.00; Centre Gallery: £10.00
Day seats (Side Gallery): £5.00**

Advance Booking, 20 April – 18 May
To book tickets during the Advance Booking period, use the Booking Form *(page 153)* or the online ticket request system (at bbc.co.uk/proms).

General Booking, from Tuesday 26 May
Once General Booking has opened, you can also book tickets by telephone or in person at Cadogan Hall (on 020 7730 4500) or at the Royal Albert Hall (on 0845 401 5040*), as well as online.

Tickets can be bought on the day of the concert – from Cadogan Hall only – from 10.00am (9.00am on Saturday 29, Sunday 30 and Monday 31 August).

£5.00 tickets on the day
At least 150 Side Gallery (bench) seats will be available for just £5.00 each from 10.00am on the day of the concert (9.00am on Saturday 29, Sunday 30 and Monday 31 August). These tickets can only be bought at Cadogan Hall. They must be purchased in person and with cash only, and are limited to two tickets per transaction.

£30.00 PCM Series Pass
Hear seven PCM concerts for just £30.00, with guaranteed entrance to the Side Gallery until 12.50pm (after which PCM Series Pass-holders may be asked to join the day queue).

PCM concerts on Saturday 29, Sunday 30 and Monday 31 August are excluded from this offer.

During the Advance Booking period (Monday 20 April – Monday 18 May), PCM Series Passes can be purchased using the Advance Booking Form *(page 153)* or the online ticket request system (at bbc.co.uk/proms). Two passport-sized photographs must be provided.

Once General Booking has opened (on Tuesday 26 May), PCM Series Passes can also be purchased by telephone or in person at the Royal Albert Hall (on 0845 401 5040*) as well as online.

Note that PCM Series Passes cannot be purchased from Cadogan Hall.

PCM Series Passes are subject to availability.

New Generation Artists 10th-Anniversary Weekend Day Tickets
Buy four tickets for the price of three: Day Tickets for Side Gallery (bench) seats will be available for just £15.00 from 9.00am on each day of the NGA 10th-Anniversary Weekend (Saturday 29, Sunday 30 and Monday 31 August). NGA Day Ticket-holders will have access to all four concerts in Cadogan Hall on that day. These tickets can only be bought at Cadogan Hall. They must be purchased in person and with cash only, and are limited to two per transaction.

ROYAL COLLEGE OF MUSIC

Prince Consort Road, London SW7 2BS
(see map, page 160) www.rcm.ac.uk

Proms Plus

Proms Plus pre-concert events will be held in the Amaryllis Fleming Concert Hall at the Royal College of Music.

All Proms Plus events are free of charge, unticketed and seating is unreserved – with the exception of the First Night live *In Tune* event on Friday 17 July, where free tickets will be available from BBC Studio Audiences (bbc.co.uk/tickets or 0370 901 1227†), and Proms Family Orchestra events, where places must be reserved in advance *(see pages 72–79)*.

Please note that all Proms Plus events are subject to capacity and we advise arriving early for the more popular events. Latecomers will be admitted but as many of these events are being recorded for broadcast, you may have to wait until a suitable moment. The event stewards will guide you.

For Prommers who join the Royal Albert Hall queue before the Proms Plus event, make sure you take a numbered slip from one of the Royal Albert Hall stewards to secure your place back in the queue.

If you have special access requirements, see Royal College of Music information opposite.

ROYAL GEOGRAPHICAL SOCIETY

Prince Consort Road, London SW7 2AR
(see map, p160) www.rgs.org

Proms Films

Proms Films are screened at the Royal Geographical Society. As with other Proms Plus events, seats are free and cannot be reserved in advance. Capacity is limited, so we advise early queuing for the more popular events. For more information, see pages 82–85. If you have special access requirements, please email house@rgs.org or phone 020 7591 3000.

†Standard geographic charges apply and calls may be included in your telecom provider's call package. Charges from mobile phones may be higher.

ACCESS AT THE PROMS

Royal Albert Hall

Please call the Access Information Line on 020 7838 3110 for advice on facilities for disabled concert-goers (including car parking) at the Royal Albert Hall, if you have any special requirements or to request a Royal Albert Hall Access Guide. Dedicated staff will be available daily from 9.00am to 9.00pm. The Access Guide is also available at www.royalalberthall.com.

The Royal Albert Hall has up to 20 spaces bookable for wheelchair-users and their companions. There are two end-of-aisle places in the Side Stalls, and two in the Centre Stalls – these places are priced as such; front-row platform places either side of the stage are priced as Side Stalls seats; rear platform places are priced as Front Circle seats. Spaces in the Front Circle are priced as such. When filling in the Booking Form, tick your preferred price range (ie Centre Stalls, Side Stalls or Front Circle) and enter the number of places required under the 'Wheelchair space' column.

Four additional wheelchair spaces are available in the Gallery for Promming. These cannot be pre-booked.

Passenger lifts at the Royal Albert Hall are located on the ground-floor corridor at Doors 1 and 8. Use of lifts is discouraged during performances.

Cadogan Hall

Cadogan Hall has a range of services to assist disabled customers, including provision for wheelchair-users in the Stalls. There are three wheelchair spaces available for advance booking and one space reserved for sale as a day ticket from 10.00am on the day of the concert (9.00am on Saturday 29, Sunday 30 and Monday 31 August). For information, call 020 7730 4500.

Royal College of Music

The Amaryllis Fleming Concert Hall at the Royal College of Music has six spaces for wheelchair-users. Direct access is now available from Prince Consort Road, located to the left of the main entrance. For further information, please call 020 7589 3643.

Discounts for Disabled Concert-Goers

Disabled concert-goers (and one companion) receive a 50% discount on all ticket prices (except Arena and Gallery areas) for concerts at the Royal Albert Hall and Cadogan Hall. To claim this discount, tick the box on the Advance Booking Form, or call the Access Information Line on 020 7838 3110 (from Tuesday 26 May) if booking by phone. Note that discounts for disabled concert-goers cannot be combined with other ticket offers. Tickets can also be purchased in person from Tuesday 26 May at the Royal Albert Hall. The Box Office is situated at Door 12 and has ramped access, an induction loop and drop-down counters.

The BBC Proms: access for all

Hard-of-Hearing and Visually Impaired Concert-Goers

The Royal Albert Hall has an infra-red system with a number of personal receivers for use with and without hearing aids. To make use of the service, collect a free receiver from the Door 6 Information Desk.

If you have a guide dog, the best place to sit in the Royal Albert Hall is in a Loggia or Second Tier Box, where your dog may stay with you. If you are sitting elsewhere, stewards will be happy to look after your dog while you enjoy the concert. Please call the Access Information Line on 020 7838 3110 in advance of your visit to organise.

Proms Guide: Non-Print Versions

Audio CD (from 27 April) and Braille (from 10 April) versions of this Guide are available in two parts, 'Articles' and 'Concert Listings/Booking Information', priced £3.00 each or £6.00 for both. For more information and to order, call RNIB Customer Services on 0845 702 3153.

Calls cost up to 4p per minute from a BT landline (plus a one-off connection charge of up to 8p). Charges from mobiles and other networks may be considerably higher.

Advance Booking

Assistance is available for visually impaired customers wishing to make Advance Booking requests. Please call the Access Information Line on 020 7838 3110.

Radio 3 Commentary

Visually impaired patrons are welcome to use the free infra-red hearing facility (see above) to listen in to the broadcast commentary on Radio 3.

Programme-Reading Service

Ask at the Door 6 Information Desk if you would like a steward to read your concert programme out to you.

Large-Print Programmes & Texts

Large-print concert programmes can be made available on the night (at the same price as the standard programme) if ordered not less than five working days in advance. Complimentary large-print texts and opera librettos (where applicable) can also be made available on the night if ordered in advance. To order any large-print programmes or texts, please call 020 7765 3246. They will be left for collection at the Door 6 Information Desk 45 minutes before the start of the concert.

GETTING THERE

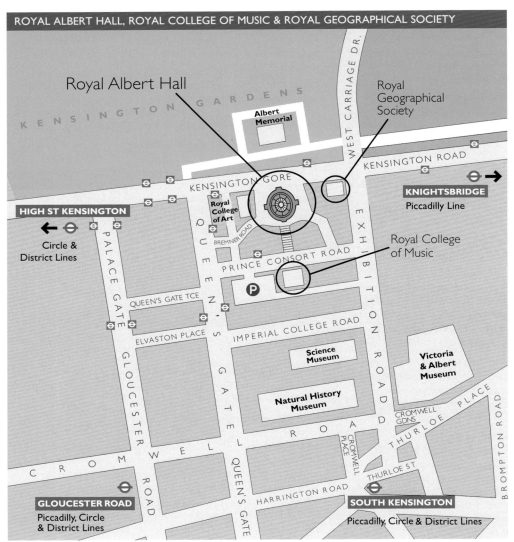

ROYAL ALBERT HALL, ROYAL COLLEGE OF MUSIC & ROYAL GEOGRAPHICAL SOCIETY

The following buses serve the Royal Albert Hall, Royal College of Music and Royal Geographical Society (via Kensington Gore, Queen's Gate, Palace Gate and/or Prince Consort Road): 9/N9, 10/N10, 49, 52/N52, 70, 360 & 452.

The following buses serve Cadogan Hall (via Sloane Street and/or Sloane Square): 11, 19, 22, 137, 211, 319, 360, 452 & C1.

For 24-hour London travel information, call 020 7222 1234 or visit www.tfl.gov.uk.

There are bicycle racks near Door 11 of the Royal Albert Hall. (Neither the Hall nor the BBC can accept responsibility for items lost or stolen from these racks.) The Royal Albert Hall is unable to accept folding bicycles in the cloakrooms.

Please note all Proms venues lie inside the Congestion Charging Zone which operates 7.00am–6.00pm Mon–Fri.

For car parking at the Royal Albert Hall, see page 157.

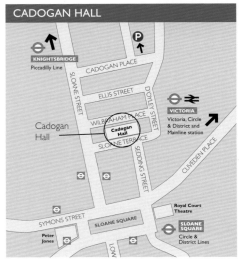

CADOGAN HALL

St Benedict's, Ealing

Independent Catholic Day School

Teaching a Way of Living

- **Excellent Academic Results**
- **Outstanding Pastoral Care**
- **Independent co-education from 3 through to 18**
- **New £6.2m complex opened in October 2008 including state-of-the-art Music facilities**
- **Scholarships and Bursaries are available**
- **The School for Ealing Abbey Choristers**

St Benedict's is proud of its uniqueness. Our mission, *'Teaching a way of living'*, defines us as a Benedictine school. Come and join us and experience our dynamic educational environment. We will have high expectations of you in everything that you do. We will equip you to deal with the challenges that life in the 21st century presents, teaching you the joys of learning whilst enabling you to retain a moral and spiritual sensibility.

To request a prospectus or make individual arrangements to visit, please contact:

Telephone: 020 8862 2254 (Senior School and Sixth Form)

Telephone: 020 8862 2054 (Nursery and Junior School)

Email: enquiries@stbenedicts.org.uk   Website: www.stbenedicts.org.uk

We respect the dignity of all and welcome students of other Christian denominations and, in the Senior School and Sixth Form, other faiths.

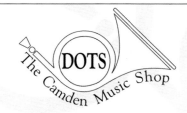

Haberdashers' Aske's School for Girls

Fun, excitement and challenge: imagination and creativity

Music & Academic Scholarships, and Bursaries up to full fees, available from 11+

Open Day 10th October 2009: 10-12am Juniors, 2-5pm Seniors

Independent Day School for Girls from 4-18

Aldenham Road, Elstree, Herts, WD6 3BT   **Registered Charity No.** 313996
e: admissions@habsgirls.org.uk **t:** 020 8266 2302 **www.habsgirls.org.uk**

The Haberdashers' Aske's Boys' School
Nurturing Excellence

An outstanding independent day school for boys aged between 5 and 18.

Open Day Saturday 10th October 1–4pm
(no appointment necessary)

Headmaster Mr Peter Hamilton MA
Butterfly Lane, Elstree, Hertfordshire WD6 3AF
Tel: 020 8266 1700 office@habsboys.org.uk

www.habsboys.org.uk
registered charity no: 313996

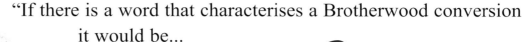
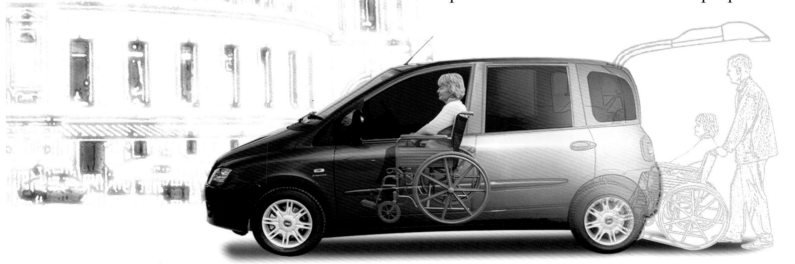

INDEX OF ARTISTS

Bold italic figures refer to Prom numbers
PCM indicates Proms Chamber Music concerts at Cadogan Hall
* first appearance at a BBC Henry Wood Promenade Concert
† current / ‡ former member of BBC Radio 3's New Generation Artists scheme

INDEX OF WORKS

BBC Proms 2009

Director Roger Wright, Controller BBC Radio 3 and Director BBC Proms
Personal Assistant Yvette Pusey

Artistic Administrator Rosemary Gent
Concerts Administrator Helen Heslop
Concerts and Events Assistant Helen Lloyd
TV Concerts Assistant Rhia Pratsis
Concerts Assistant Catherine Langston

Head of Marketing, Publications and Learning Kate Finch
Publicist Victoria Bevan
Publicity Assistant Bethan Bide

Marketing Co-ordinator Catherine Cook

Learning Manager Ellara Wakely
Learning and Audience Development Co-ordinator Naomi Selwyn

Management Assistant Tricia Twigg
Business Assistant Sally Drinkwater

Editor, BBC Radio 3 Edward Blakeman
Editor, TV Classical Music Oliver Macfarlane

BBC Proms 2009 Guide

Editor Edward Bhesania
Design Premm Design Ltd, London
Cover illustration © Andy Potts

Publications Editor John Bryant
Publications Designer Tania Conrad
Sub-Editor Clara Nissen
Publications Officer Lydia Casey

Published by BBC Proms Publications, Room 1045, Broadcasting House, London W1A 1AA

Distributed by BBC Books, an imprint of Ebury Publishing, a Random House Group Company, 20 Vauxhall Bridge Road, London SW1V 2SA

Advertising Cabbell Publishing Ltd, London (020 8971 8450)

Printed by ESP Colour, Swindon
ESP holds the Environmental Standard ISO 14001

© BBC 2009. All details were correct at time of going to press.
ISBN 978-1-84607-788-3